PROBLEMS OF
THE MIDDLE-AGED

PROBLEMS OF
THE MIDDLE-AGED

Compiled by

CLYDE B. VEDDER, Ph.D.

Professor, Department of Sociology and Anthropology
Northern Illinois University
DeKalb, Illinois

CHARLES C THOMAS · **PUBLISHER**
Springfield · *Illinois* · *U.S.A.*

Published and Distributed Throughout the World by

CHARLES C THOMAS • PUBLISHER

BANNERSTONE HOUSE

301-327 East Lawrence Avenue, Springfield, Illinois, U.S.A.

NATCHEZ PLANTATION HOUSE

735 North Atlantic Boulevard, Fort Lauderdale, Florida, U.S.A.

*With THOMAS BOOKS careful attention is given to all details of
manufacturing and design. It is the Publisher's desire to present books
that are satisfactory as to their physical qualities and artistic possibilities
and appropriate for their particular use. THOMAS BOOKS will be true
to those laws of quality that assure a good name and good will.*

Printed in the United States of America

T-1

AUTHORS

ROBERT W. ADAMS, JR., M.D.
Assistant Professor
Department of Psychiatry
Vanderbilt University Medical School
Nashville, Tennessee

WALTER C. ALVAREZ, M.D.
Chicago, Illinois

LELAND J. AXELSON, Ph.D.
Washington State University
Pullman, Washington

JOHN W. BALLEW, M.D.
Assistant Resident
Department of Obstetrics and Gynecology
Washington University School of Medicine
St. Louis, Missouri

OTTO BILLIG, M.D.
Associate Professor
Department of Psychiatry
Vanderbilt University Medical School
Nashville, Tennessee

JAMES O. BOND, M.D.
Epidemiologist
Florida State Board of Health
Jacksonville, Florida

ADOLPH M. BROWN, M.D.*
Beverly Hills, California

RUTH SHONLE CAVAN, Ph.D.
Professor Emeritus of Sociology
Rockford College
Rockford, Illinois

* Deceased.

[v]

THOMAS C. DESMOND
New York, New York

DAVID C. GARRON
Lecturer
Committee on Human Development
University of Chicago
Chicago, Illinois

JOHN E. GIBSON
New York, New York

RAY GILES
New York, New York

ELMER HESS, M.D.
Erie, Pennsylvania

ANTHONY F. KAMINSKY, M.D.*
Erie, Pennsylvania

"ANN LEIGHTON"
(Pseudonym)

ALBERT J. LEVINE, Ph.D.
Skokie, Illinois

WILLIAM H. MASTERS, M.D.
Associate Professor
Department of Obstetrics and Gynecology
Washington University School of Medicine
St. Louis, Missouri

RICHARD I. MILLER, Ed.D.
Instructor in Education
and Physical Education
University of Illinois
Urbana, Illinois

BERNICE L. NEUGARTEN, Ph.D.
Assistant Professor
Committee on Human Development
University of Chicago
Chicago, Illinois

---

* Deceased.

CHARLES E. ODELL
Director
Older and Retired Workers Department
International Union, U.A.W.
Detroit, Michigan

ARNOLD M. ROSE, Ph.D.
University of Minnesota
Minneapolis, Minnesota

ARTHUR M. ROSS
University of California
Berkeley, California

JANE N. ROSS
University of California
Berkeley, California

RUSSELL B. ROTH, M.D.
Erie, Pennsylvania

J. S. SLOTKIN, Ph.D.
University of Chicago
Chicago, Illinois

PETER J. STEINCROHN, M.D.
Formerly Chief of Staff
Mt. Sinai Hospital
Hartford, Connecticut

MARVIN B. SUSSMAN, Ph.D.
Department of Sociology
Western Reserve University
Cleveland, Ohio

FREDERIC W. TERRIEN, Ph.D.
Associate Professor of Sociology
San Francisco State College
San Francisco, California

LLOYD JAMES THOMPSON, M.D.
Winston Salem, North Carolina

HOWARD WHITMAN
Des Moines, Iowa

PREFACE

THE great unmet challenge to gerontology lies in . . . Middle Age. Many texts delineate middle age as those years between 30-60, but demographers prefer the years 45-64, since retirement at 65 is a good index for the end of middle age, as age 65 signifies entrance into old age. Textbooks in the field of gerontology concentrate on old age and its problems, but the basis of most problems probably originate during the middle years, or even before. It is due to this lack of academic interest that the middle-years, 45-64 are the least understood phase of the life cycle.

Very few academicians and professional journalists have addressed themselves to middle-age and its problems. Milton L. Barron in *The Aging American* directs attention to the social-psychological problems, some health problems and research hypothesis of middle age. Clark Tibbitts and Wilma Donahue (Eds.) in *Aging in Today's Society* indicate that middle-age is an age of opportunity. The middle-aged are the explorers, the pioneers of the new "prime of life." L. Gernant in *You're Older Than You Think* indicates that the challenge of middle-age is to get ready for the later years, not to be satisfied with the pre-dinner coctail, after-dinner nap, evening newspaper, followed by a late-late movie on television. These time-consuming routines are the most tranquil, uninspiring and most devastating set of habits one can get into, while failing to prepare for living twenty-five years ahead. The middle-aged, especially the single, widowed and the divorced cannot afford psychologically to ignore family ties and go it alone. Natalie Harris Cabot in *You Can't Count on Dying* asks why middle-aged people cannot retire *for* as well as *from* something? E. J. Stieglitz in *The Second*

Forty Years believed that the gerontologist should give his attention to the adult period of middle-age (45-64) rather than after 65, because at age 65 and over life is too far gone for the person to render much service. Good practical advice and suggestions to middle-aged individuals may be found in *The Golden Years* by Thomas Collins, in various published booklet forms which are nationally advertised.

In the years to come, it is anticipated that more research will be directed toward the middle-aged group, who in 1965 number over 32 million individuals, an increase of 193 per cent for this age group compared with a 98 per cent increase of the total population since 1900. As pointed out by Tibbitts and Donahue, the American culture today is focused on two sets of people; the young adults with children, and the elders. But it is those in the middle years who create and manage the society for both of the others.

Only recently, "A Prayer for the Middle Aged" was noted, authorship unknown, which is hereby reproduced:

Lord, thou knowest better than I know myself that I am growing older and will some day be old. Keep me from the fatal habit of thinking I must say something on every subject and on every occasion. Release me from craving to straighten out everybody's affairs. Make me thoughtful but not moody; helpful but not bossy. With my vast store of wisdom, it seems a pity not to use it all, but thou knowest, Lord, that I want a few friends at the end.

Keep my mind free from the recital of endless details; give me wings to get to the point. Seal my lips on my aches and pains. They are increasing and love of rehearsing them is becoming sweeter as the years go by. I dare not ask grace enough to enjoy the tales of another's pains, but help me to endure them with patience.

I dare not ask for improved memory, but for a growing humility and less cocksureness when my memory seems to clash with the memories of others. Teach me the glorious lesson that occasionally I may be mistaken. Keep me reasonably sweet; I do not want to be a saint—some of them are so hard to live with—but a sour old person is one of the crowning works of the devil. Give me the ability to see good things in unexpected places and talents in unexpected people. Give me the grace to tell them so. Amen.

CONTENTS

PROBLEMS OF
THE MIDDLE-AGED

AMERICA'S UNKNOWN MIDDLE-AGERS[*]
THOMAS C. DESMOND

AMERICANS slump into middle age grudgingly, sadly, and with a tinge of fear. As a result of this immature reaction to maturity we carelessly fritter away what should be truly "the prime of life." The late Dr. Martin Gumpert, one of the nation's foremost experts on aging, was convinced not only that most Americans waste their middle years but that this ruins their chances of happiness and usefulness in their later years.

Many of the 35,000,000 Americans between the ages of 40 and 60, commonly though uncritically designated as the period of "middle age," are likely to identify themselves psychologically with the aging comedian Jack Benny. For years he has drawn guffaws by his blend of pathetic and ludicrous insistence that he is no more than 39. And Walter Pitkin made publishing history with a best seller which assured Americans that *Life Begins at Forty* — because apparently so many are certain life really ends at mid-life.

Whether or not Benny's is actually the common reaction to it, middle age is certainly the least understood phase of the life cycle, and, in terms of its opportunities, the most misunderstood.

Fortunately, new research is being launched to appraise the assets of middle life and place in our hands facts which may help break down our irrational attitudes toward being middle-aged. Science and government are teaming up to attack for the first time our lack of knowledge of the possibilities of middle age. Typifying the trend are recent conferences that have dealt with various aspects of the subject.

---

[*] *New York Times* Magazine, July 29, 1956.

[3]

One of these known as the Bethesda Conference, brought together experts in biology, sociology and psychology who recommended a redirection of research toward the *potentials* of middle life instead of emphasizing tests which spotlight decay and decline. Another was a Federal-State Conference on Aging, where it was noted that if we are ever to solve the plight of old folks who want to continue working we must turn attention to the problems of the workers aged 40 to 60. The New York State Joint Legislative Committee on Problems of the Aging also recently urged educators, psychiatrists and health agencies to give greater attention to the middle period of the life cycle.

On a broad plane the problem is being approached from two sides. Gerontologists, the old-age experts, are reaching down into the middle years to explore preventive measures that will assure that the later years will be a treat rather than a retreat, and, at the other end of the scale, child psychologists, who in increasing numbers are turning to the study of middle age, are using techniques they evolved for the study of youngsters. Just as pediatrics emerged to center attention on the care of children, so a new discipline of "mediatrics" may blossom forth to care for middle-aged folks.

What is a valid picture of America's middle-aged?

Actually we know very little about this because middle age is a relatively new mass phenomenon. In prehistoric times man lived on an average about eighteen years. Fossil remains indicate that few lived beyond forty. Even as recently as 1900 life expectancy was about 45, and only 10 per cent of the population was middle-aged. Our knowledge of the subject is skimpy because science has not yet had time to conduct many life-span studies on humans. And yet today four out of five of us survive to at least 60, and the average adult in our labor force is 45. While our total population increased 98 per cent in the last half century, our middle agers increased by 200 per cent.

Scientists appreciate the fact that "middle age" is a layman's term, embracing a multitude of different attributes which seem noticeable mainly between 40 and 60. However, a recent study of 3,515 workers aged 63 and 64 revealed that two out of three of them think they are "middle-aged or younger." Perhaps many of them are, in terms of potential life span or their own capabilities. Individuals age at different rates. George Bernard Shaw, lamenting his arrival at middle age, was told by a perceptive young lady: "Middle age? Forty is nothing in an Irishman."

One view of the middle-aged depicts the male as an ulcer-coddling, tension-ridden, dollar-mad, sex-obsessed, culture-anemic individual too busy making a living to live. The American female middle-ager is often charged with being mainly concerned with such matters as double chins, seven-day diets, her husband's waning ardor, her children's rebelliousness and Gregory Peck's latest starring role. Are these facts or caricatures?

Certainly we need not accept this as "normal" middle age without considerable reservation. Today, for example, in New York State alone an estimated 150,000 middle-aged people are enrolled in adult education courses. Doesn't this indicate that large numbers of middle-agers are still growing intellectually, are serious minded and flexible? Over 5,000,000 middle-aged women are in the nation's labor force. Many of them are maintaining the triple roles of mother-wife-earner.

Middle age is for some a frantic rush. It's trying to land the top job in the office, financing the children through college, worrying about one's marriage, meeting the bills that pile up. For others it's rounds of golf, games of bridge, a whirl at guiding the teen-agers, P. T. A., church, social and business meetings — and the days fly by as they never did in earlier times. And suddenly, the middle years are irretrievably gone.

But here again we can only say this is probably a portrait of some middle-class middle-aged. Our social scientists have done practically no probing among either the lower or upper income middle-agers, and very little among the middle income group.

The middle-aged man is likely to be near his peak of earning power. The latest data indicate that the man 55-64, for example, had in 1952 a median income a shade below the peak for the 35-44-year-olds. For professional people, business men and skilled artisans, middle age is often the period of top earnings. Despite the woes it has obtaining work once it is unemployed, middle age is 93 per cent employed. Records indicate that the middle-aged are absent less, are more reliable, and rack up better ratings from supervisors than do younger age groups. And almost 95 per cent of those 45-64 are not disabled and can work.

Middle age is family life. Over 80 per cent of our middle-aged men and more than 70 per cent of the women are married. Only 8 per cent of the middle-agers are spinsters or bachelors. These statistics, however, under-emphasize the fact that the crisis period for marital happiness has been found to be in the late forties and early fifties for women and in the fifties for men. This is the period of the empty or emptying nest, when the children one has fed, dressed, scolded, advised and cajoled fly from home.

Middle age is still capable of mental growth. Classic studies have indicated that general intelligence grows until the age of 16 on a straight linear basis, then continues to grow at a slower pace until about 21, at which age a very gradual decline in rate of learning may set in until at 55 the rate drops to the 14-year-old rate. (This does not mean level of intelligence; it means *rate of ability to learn* — and a 14-year-old can learn very rapidly indeed.)

It is significant, however, that these old, accepted studies are now being challenged. Dr. William A. Owens of Iowa State College, for instance, has tested middle-agers who had previously been examined at the age of 19 and found not a decline but a significant increase in total score, with more than one-third of the 45-49 age group scoring better than the average of the 19-21-year-olds. Middle age scores poorly on sentence completion tests and on analogical thinking, but makes high scores on general information and vocabulary tests and does not slip much on arithmetical problems.

Flexibility, physical and mental, may diminish, but to what extent we do not know. An experiment at Cambridge University involved a group of persons from 14 to 60 years old who were asked to throw links of chain at a target — first tossing the chain directly at the target, then over a bar in front of the target, and finally aiming it at the target through a mirror that reversed the near-far dimensions of the target. What were the results?

Only in the mirror test did the middle-aged slump behind the younger folk. The psychologists assume that the mirror test calls for a fresh organization of incoming stimuli. It was only when this new situation was introduced that the middle-aged could not meet the challenge of the youngsters.

Whatever the handicaps of middle age, they do not appear to be any more formidable than those which confront any other phase of life cycle. Life at all stages is a continuum in which we give up some things, gain other things.

Middle age does, however — and let us admit it — have some special handicaps of its own, chiefly man-made. Middle age loses power, speed and glamour and, to the immature adult, these may be profound blows to his ego.

Psychologists know that strength, as tested by hand-grip, pulling power and swiftness of blow, begins to decline in the mid-twenties, although a Sugar Ray Robinson occasionally comes along to prove somewhat exceptional. They have found that steering coordination declines from a peak at 20; that braking reaction time is quickest at 25, then declines rapidly. The middle-aged person often finds he can no longer read small print without glasses.

Recuperative powers of the middle-ager are substantial, but not quite what they were in younger days. At 20, you can stay out until 3 A.M. and still be at the office at 9 without the boss or you knowing the difference; but in middle age, if you are out after midnight, it may take a day or two to regain normal efficiency. The skin wound that heals on a 20-year-old in seven days heals for a 40-year-old in fourteen days.

Yet actually there are no mental or physical slippages which should mean any significant handicap for middle age. And what we lose in stamina, and in the ego picture of ourselves as our heads grow balder, we gain in experience, maturity and wisdom.

The main threats to adjustment in middle life appear to be

"middle age fatigue," "middle age discontent" and "middle age boredom."

Undoubtedly some people of middle age, at the peak of their earning power, begin to find younger men coming up, challenging their position and authority and know-how. For men with responsibilities, for those striving for achievement and success, middle age can be rough. But, ironically, those in low competitive, low economic groupings find that love and approval are not conditioned on "success."

The breaking of identification with our children that comes with middle life is often a deep traumatic experience. The boredom that frequently develops at this stage may arise when the children leave home and husband and wife are suddenly left facing each other alone for the first time since early marriage. They find they have no interests in common, no hobbies, no urgent goals. A recent study indicated that the most balanced and happiest middle-aged couples tend to be those who avert this boredom by active work in civic, social and church groups.

In this period both men and women are often assailed by moodiness and irritability, sometimes panic. A survey I conducted indicated that most persons working at 65 moved on from their previous jobs in their middle forties, and we suspect that this is caused less by economic factors than by middle-age discontent.

One of the main handicaps of middle age is our devotion to the cult of youth. We appear terrorized by wrinkle; a gray hair is a rebuke. This in turn leads to the "no one over 40 wanted" qualifications on jobs, even in tight labor markets. Because of this youth cult many middle-aged women flee to hair dyers, color rinsers and facial uplifters.

From any really objective viewpoint, from any sound perspective, however, middle age has advantages which far outweigh its disadvantages.

Middle age in our Western civilization has three major roles: (1) realization of its own potential in terms of achievement and satisfactions, (2) completion of care of the younger generation and fitting them for independence and (3) preparation for the later years.

To attain its goals, middle age is perhaps better equipped to reach its objectives than any other stage in the life cycle. That is why poets like Carolyn Wells comment:

> *"Youth is a silly vapid state;*
> *Old age with fears and ills is rife.*
> *This simple boon I beg of fate —*
> *A thousand years of middle life."*

Hervey Allen in "Anthony Adverse" says: "Grow up as soon as you can. It pays. The only time you really live is from 30 to 60. The young are slaves of dreams; the old, servants of regrets. Only the middle-aged have all their five senses in the keeping of their wits." Although these are over-distortions of the drawbacks of youth and old age, we need such reminders of the strength of the middle years.

Middle age is not headlong. The impetuosity of youth which rushes it madly into life-traps is gone. Instead, middle age can cope with its tensions and pressures by drawing upon its varied experience, by calmly evaluating alternatives. Physically well, mentally alert, middle age should prove up to the problems that beset it.

If we lose our figures and our hair becomes speckled with gray, we have at least gained status in our community. Middle age has an accepted role in our society. It has more opportunity for service. The middle-aged man often finds himself serving on community committees, on church and professional boards.

Middle age has enough perspective not to be led astray by the tawdry and shallow, nor by glitter and tinsel, but rather to search for what is true and of value. Fortunately, in middle age, man is afforded an opportunity to assess not only the errors of the past but also the opportunities that lie ahead. It is as though in the mysterious pattern of nature, man is given a second chance to make of his life something good, something rewarding.

It gives him an opportunity to prevent his later years from being crabbed and wretched.

We see this spirit of reassessment of life's goal in the middle-aged mother who decides she would like to go back to college to earn her teaching license, the middle-aged reporter who gives up a glamorous, well-paying job as Capitol correspondent for a lower-paying post teaching journalism. It is more than external change. The business man who quit his steel concern to enter the ministry and the woman in her fifties who works every day as a volunteer in a hospital are redirecting themselves internally.

For middle age more and more seems to ask: "What is worthy?" rather than "What is it worth?" Herein middle age distinguishes itself from young adulthood.

Middle age is the period of synthesis. Neither green nor over-ripe, middle age can weld together its past experiences into a meaningful whole. The middle-aged scientist is still creative, but he often is also interested in giving broader meaning to isolated experiments. Young adulthood is usually too preoccupied with its pleasures and demands of the moment to view life as a whole. Middle age draws meaning out of life.

Middle age is not so much "settled" as matured. It can change, but will not without good cause. Some middle-agers are inflexible, but not because they are middle-aged. They were old before their time. Middle age isn't interested in newness for the sake of newness, nor in learning tricks for the sake of learn-ing new tricks. The alleged inflexibility of middle age is really quite often a subtle protest against futile change for change's sake. Patterns of life established in the twenties and thirties can be altered if there is sufficient motivation. Although teen-agers undoubtedly think their parents are "old dodos," they misread the signs.

If middle age were as reckless as the twenties and thirties, our economic and social civilization would be catapulted to-ward every new panacea, every bright promise. If middle age were as backward-looking as old age we would hardly move at all. Middle age is needed as a bulwark against youth's recklessness and age's conservatism. Middle age is not conservative so much as deliberate and judicial. In middle life we look ahead as much as we look backward.

Most gerontologists tend to view life as a climb up a mountain, with the peak reached in later years. In this perspective, middle age is a high plateau where man reassesses his route, enjoys the adventure, skirts the pitfalls. There is less expending of self on meaningless frivolities. There is in middle life a search for satisfying relationships with others and between one's self and destiny.

Here we become adjusted to not attaining the youthful goals we set for ourselves. This is the period of balance between activity and contemplation. Like big league pitchers who as they age turn from throwing speed balls to reliance on change of pace and control, the middle-ager, out of his bag of experience, calls upon varied resources built of past successes and failures.

Middle age is fortified by economic strength not possessed by youth. What middle age lacks in physical strength it can compensate for with improved economic know-how. Middle age generally has already made a substantial investment in life and can start drawing its dividends. Middle age is not the "medicine" to be taken to survive to later years. It is the rich dessert on the menu of life.

The emerging concern of science with middle age will give us new tools better to understand ourselves in the middle years, new armament with which to fortify ourselves for the strains of middle life. Yet we need not wait for science's discoveries; much of the discoveries lie before us in ourselves, for ourselves to uncover.

ATTITUDES OF MIDDLE-AGED PERSONS TOWARD GROWING OLDER*

BERNICE L. NEUGARTEN, Ph.D., and DAVID C. GARRON

THIS study of attitudes toward aging is based upon interviews with a sample of 625 men and women aged 40 to 70 residing in the metropolitan area of Kansas City. The group constituted a random sample of individuals (not married couples) drawn by area-probability technics and stratified by age, sex, and social status. The sample was approximately equally divided between men and women as well as among persons of each of four social-class levels, ranging from upper-middle to lower-lower; there were approximately equal numbers in each five-year age interval from 40 to 44 to 65 and over.

SURVEY TECHNIC

Data were gathered in connection with a larger study, the Kansas City Study of Adult Life. In an extensive interview exploring the present and past life pattern, a number of questions were asked regarding attitudes toward the present and toward the future. The respondent was asked to tell how he felt about being his present age; to compare his health to other people of the same age; and to name his age group as "young," "middle-age," "old," or any other term he found appropriate. This question was followed by others asking when he had begun to feel whatever age he termed himself and why; how he had changed most in the past ten years; and how he felt about growing older. He was then asked what he thought life would be like as he grew older, and what he considered the happiest time of his life as well as the elements that made it so.

* Geriatrics, 14:21-24, January 1959.

ANALYSIS OF INTERVIEW DATA

Each interview was analyzed from several points of view: What was the quality of the affect expressed? Did the respondent evaluate the present, and did he see the future in positive or in negative terms? What were the factors associated with and what the reasons given for positive or negative attitudes? In making judgments about the respondent's attitudes, the entire interview was read with special attention given to the questions just described.

Upon analysis of their attitudes toward the present, the respondents were placed in one of three categories — positive, negative, or neutral. Those whose feelings were actually neutral in tone were placed in the neutral category as well as those whose responses were noncommital or evasive. The usual neutral response was "Things are O.K., about the same as they have always been." As the authors were interested only in expressed attitudes, no attempt was made to force a negative or positive evaluation of those responses in which the respondent had avoided an evaluation.

Attitudes toward the future were placed in one of four categories: positive, negative, neutral, or contingent. The contingent responses were those in which the respondent said, in effect, "Growing older will be fine if my health stays good" or "I don't mind growing old as long as I don't become a burden to anyone."

The data were further analyzed by determining the relationship between gross social variables and attitudinal patterns. For example, the sexes were compared to see if the distribution of positive, negative, and neutral attitudes toward the present and future was different for men than for women. The respondents were compared by age to see if the 60-year-olds gave more negative responses about the future than did the 40-year-olds. Women who were mothers and grandmothers were compared with women who had remained childless.

A number of other factors were similarly isolated. The following factors were dealt with singly and in combination, using all combinations that seemed theoretically meaningful: sex, age, social class, health report, marital status, parenthood, and grand-parenthood.

The chi-square test was applied to the distributions obtained; only those distributions stable at or beyond the .05 level are reported.

FINDINGS AND DISCUSSION OF RESULTS

Attitudes toward the present were classified as neutral in 55 per cent of the 625 persons interviewed, positive in 28 per cent, and negative in 17 per cent. Attitudes toward the future were positive in 14 per cent, negative in 13 per cent, contingent in 18 per cent, and, again, neutral in 55 per cent. There was, as might have been expected, a consistent relationship between attitudes toward the present and toward the future — that is, here was a reliable tendency for those with positive attitudes about the present to look toward the future with optimism and vice versa.

The large proportion of neutral responses is perhaps not surprising. For some persons, life has a certain blandness and cannot be described in strong emotional terms or by comparing one period of life with another. For most people, there are few reference points by which to describe anticipations. Many people, given neither to introspection nor to continual evaluation of experience, are taken aback by the inquiries and give non-committal replies not only to single questions but to whole series of questions.

There is also the factor that the researcher may suffer from a cautious and gingerly approach to questions about aging. Had the interviewers been able to overcome their own hesitancies and biases about aging and had they questioned and probed in areas not necessarily sensitive for the subject, the data would undoubtedly have been richer.

We found only a few relationships between social variables and attitudes toward the present and the future:

1) A small group (both men and women), composing only 12 per cent of the whole, considered their health to be worse than that of other persons of the same age. This group showed

a higher proportion of negative attitudes toward the present than the sample at large, as well as a higher proportion of negative attitudes toward the future.

2) Older women (aged 55 to 70) of all social classes reported more negative health than expected — an age difference not found in the male subsample.

3) When all the women in the sample were subjected to further analysis, it was found that those not living with a spouse (that is, single, widowed, divorced, or separated) and also unemployed tended to report more negative health, negative present, negative future, and contingent future attitudes. Women who were both married and employed tended to report less negative health than expected and more positive attitudes about the present. (A similar analysis could not be made for the men because there were so few who were unemployed in the sample.)

These are the only relationships found between the social variables and affective evaluations of life. It is striking that, with these few exceptions, attitudes toward the present and future did not vary consistently with any single or any combination of the social variables studied. The conclusion seems warranted, then, that for the typical middle-aged adult, attitudes toward aging depend upon an idiosyncratic pattern of social and psychologic factors. These attitudes cannot be predicted on the basis of one or more gross sociologic factors.

These findings are perhaps of less value in themselves than for the implications they hold. To understand attitude about aging, and probably other aspects of aging as well, research workers might well turn away from such gross variables as those dealt with here and give attention instead to delineation of more subtle patterns of social interaction and personality.

To turn to an analysis of the content rather than the tone of the responses, there was little consistency in the reasons given for either positive or negative evaluations of the present. The events and situations associated with positive and negative outlooks are highly idiosyncratic. To illustrate with extreme examples, one woman reports that life is miserable because of continued poor health, while another, who has just suffered permanent and crippling injuries in an accident, reports that the present is the happiest time of her life because she feels lucky to be alive.

On the other hand, there was a striking consistency in the content of responses about the future. For those persons expressing negative or contingent attitudes toward the future, the fear of some form of dependency is paramount. They say: "Growing old is terrible, because somebody has to take care of you," or "I don't mind growing old as long as I don't become a burden to others." Dependency in turn is always seen as having two sources — loss of income and loss of health. Seldom is one mentioned without the other. Fear of death is never alluded to, nor is fear of social isolation. Illness, blindness, and deafness are seen not as threats to bodily integrity, but as states involving dependence upon others.

This triad — dependency, loss of health, and loss of income — was the only theme to occur with any frequency. It is of special interest that the incidence of this response was approximately the same for men as for women, for the different social classes, and for people at all ages. Since the 40-year-old mentions the dependency triad as frequently as does the 60-year-old, it appears that he interprets the question about growing older as referring to a period of "being aged," and not to the near or relatively near years of 50s and 60s. Thus, for all people, "becoming older" does not appear problematic — it is "being old" that has meaning.

IMPLICATIONS

One point merits further comment, as it bears upon much of the present research in gerontology. Several facts — that there were no over-all age differences in these data; that the 60-year olds gave no higher frequency of pessimistic responses about the present or toward the future; that for those who did respond negatively, the responses showed the same variety for the 60-year-olds as they did for the 40-year-olds; that worries about the future, expressed either as negative or contingent responses, showed the same consistencies for the 40-year-olds as for the 60-year-olds — all seem to have significance for future research.

While investigators must be cautious in generalizing from data to other areas and aspects of research on aging, these findings parallel others now being obtained from the Kansas City Study of Adult Life. They corroborate our general impression that chronologic age is not a meaningful variable by which to order most social and psychologic data on the middle years of life.

Social patterns, personality patterns, and styles of aging — all seem to vary independently of chronologic age. If this proves true in other populations, then gerontologists shall have to stop linking the terms "age" and "aging" as if these phenomena were necessarily related. To repeat, we must attempt to discover the social and psychologic processes that are *relevant* to aging and to use these rather than chronologic age to orient our research.

EXERCISE AFTER 40? FORGET IT!*

PETER J. STEINCROHN, M.D.

A PLEASURABLE feeling of relaxation should set in at about 40 years of age, but hundreds of thousands of neurotic Americans just won't let nature take its course. Unfortunately they believe that they *must* exercise. As a physician, I am convinced that exercise is unnecessary — and often harmful.

I know a man of 50 who pointed out a heavily rouged elderly woman and said, "Isn't it too bad that some people can't accept age with good grace?" Yet this same man hurries to the gym every day except Sunday and subjects his body to a cruel mauling.

Ask him why and he answers, "I don't know whether exercise is good or bad. But I'm not going to give in to the easy life just because I've turned 50. Besides, my doctor prescribed it for me because I'm so tense and nervous. He wants me to work it off."

The truth is that the elderly woman who tries to hold onto youth by using an extra layer of rouge merits less censure than the middle-aged man who deliberately ignores the groans of his complaining muscles.

Too many Americans are exercise-mad. They wave their arms and legs in ridiculous circles and angles; they twist and turn their torsos into a semblance of half-formed pretzels; they concentrate a week of golf (because they have little time) into a Sunday marathon of 36 to 54 holes; they walk like a lamb to a workout at the gym, rush out feeling like a lion — and wind up at home that night too limp and exhausted to be fit companions the rest of the evening.

* *Science Digest,* 26:5:1-6, November 1949. Condensed from Steincrohn, Peter J.:*You and Your Fears.* Doubleday & Co., 1948, 1949.

Some do it because they like it; too many because they think it will relax them and cure their anxieties.

A report in 1943 by a committee of the American Association for Health, Physical Education and Recreation (assisted by a committee of consultants appointed by the American Medical Association) is enlightening. It read in part: "Among older persons (over 40) physical examinations and observations of the individual's reaction to exercise will disclose large numbers who need to restrict exercise."

In other words, if you must exercise, at least be reasonably certain that you are healthy enough to undergo its rigors. And remember that the fact that you feel well is no proof that you are well. A thorough annual physical checkup is the only sensible answer to that question.

Exercise, like rheumatism, is a vague term. Just what is it? It may be defined as any type of strenuous exertion that the human being engages in for the sole purpose of preserving or improving his fitness, health, or appearance.

Without question, exercise is all right for growing children, young adults, and patients with deformities and other medical handicaps; for example, in those suffering from arthritis or in patients recovering from fractures.

Physicians often prescribe, and rightly, underwater exercise (hydrogymnastics) for those who have infantile paralysis or spinal deformities.

But exercise isn't a "cure-all" for tenseness and anxiety. You can't blunt the frayed nerves in your head by wearing out the soles of your feet.

After 40, exercise should not be taken so complacently as the cream in your coffee or the dressing on your salad. Too many of us think we are as fit as we ever were and therefore feel the need for exercise to maintain that fitness. Tragedy often results.

For example, some time ago the press carried front-page news of the sudden death, in his early 50's, of one of Hollywood's best-known men.

About five years ago I quoted him in a book I wrote. In effect he had said, "Although I am now over 40, I can run several miles with ease and my appetite is that of a youngster's. I attribute my excellent physical condition to periodic exercises."

I remember predicting at the time that he was lowering his normal life expectancy. Unfortunately he proved to be one of many such cases that really should be chalked up as "slow suicide."

Of course there are the usual exceptions that prove the rule. The picture of the King of Sweden with tennis racquet comes to mind first. Another example is that of an 84-year-old lady who came to my office. Examination disclosed a weak heart that was doing a tolerable job for an octogenarian.

Later, on her way out of the office she turned back to ask, "By the way, Doctor, is it all right for me to keep up my horseback riding? I have been riding three times a week for years." I crossed my fingers and said, "Fine, keep it up," recalling the old wheeze about Grandfather, who died at the early age of 99 because his horse reared up and threw him.

Another exception is the 75-year-old man with blood pressure over 250, who continued to swim and dive without apparent damage to his circulation. But such cases are rarities. For each one, there are hundreds that reinforce the view that unnecessary exertion terminates life prematurely.

If you are considering a course of exercise, think of your heart. This organ requires careful consideration when you undertake exertion. It deserves as much rest and relaxation as it can wheedle out of you. It is definitely not a tireless worker.

If you weigh 150 pounds, about 70 pounds are muscle; and only about one-half pound is your heart. When you are at rest the heart pumps out three to four quarts of blood per minute. During strenuous exercise it may put out 19 to 37 quarts a minute.

If you could transform your heart into a miniature derrick, its power could lift you three and one-half feet into the air every minute.

You may ask, "Isn't it true that strenuous exertion will not 'strain' the healthy heart?" Drs. H. L. Smith of the Mayo Clinic and William G. Leaman of the University of Pennsylvania a few years ago agreed that the healthy heart can take it. And this is accepted by the medical profession today.

But we should remember that a healthy 40-year-old heart can become a sick heart when asked to carry a 20-year-old's burden.

If you were never an outstanding athlete, do not hope to make up for it in middle age. Any man over 40 who exercises or takes up sports with the thought of relieving tension of demonstrating to himself or others that he is a Hercules deserves a different appellation: that of a senile Samson with bobbed haircut.

Do you enjoy your golf? Then play it — but don't work at it. If you must hurry through your job to keep a date at the course; if you must rush through 18 holes because you don't want your wife to be fretting about a cold dinner; then you are actually under strain and tension, while at work, on the course, and at dinner.

The ideal way to play at any game is to finish your business leisurely, drive slowly to your appointment, dawdle while you play, dawdle through a shower, and then still have sufficient time left over for a hot dinner at home.

If you relax more often, if you slow up, don't believe that you will grow old prematurely. The grim reaper won't swish his scythe at you and cut you off long before you reach the 70s and 80s. On the contrary, the reaper seems to have patience for the relaxers and is impatient with the overdoers.

In that connection it is interesting that follow-up studies have shown that Phi Beta Kappas live longer than their fellow students. They have been content, in most cases, to be onlookers and not participants in sport, at college or in later years.

The lazier you tend to be, the better for you. If you won your letter in high school or college, don't believe that if you stop exercising you will get "fat around the heart." Augustus Thorndike, Jr., M.D., of Harvard, who followed and treated athletes there for many years, discarded the old chestnut, "ex-football players get fat."

All this is contrary to the loosely held belief that "you can't be healthy without exercise." Somehow the misbelief has also become prevalent that the man who keeps fit with exercise is less liable to contract or succumb to disease.

On the contrary, you can be healthy without crooking a little finger in exercise.

Too many persons believe that such fitness, which is supposed to be the result of exercise, is the fortress impregnable against the millions of bacteria that are forever trying to infiltrate our defenses. Microbes shown no more respect for a Mr. Tarzan than for a Mr. Milquetoast.

What greater proof is there that middle-aged bones, muscles, nerves, and hearts can't take it than the experience of the armed forces during the past war? Thousands of middle-aged men received a "lift" when they were invited to join right up to the age of 45.

As weeks and months passed, however, word came by the grapevine that the "old men" weren't standing up to the kids. I received word from a friend, a colonel in charge of a military hospital, that too many of the hospital beds were occupied by middle-aged men who had collapsed during maneuvers. Their bodies were not fit even for a bloodless war. It wasn't long before the higher-ups in Washington added two and two. Age limits were reduced from 45 to 38.

If you are over 40 you are in the company of at least 50 million other Americans who have lived through half their physical allotment of years. Whereas Youth often wastes his energy, he can afford to. He is like a rubber ball that keeps bouncing with unimpaired elasticity.

But Middle Age must conserve his energy surplus because the elasticity just isn't there. In fact at the age of 60 a person has 50 per cent less efficiency than at the age of ten. Not only his arteries but his nerves become secondhand fixtures.

Suppose you know you are healthy. Even then there's no sense in trying to take 150 per cent energy out of a 100 per cent machine. And further, if your doctor has found that you are slipping a little, it is equally true that you can't expect to take 100 per cent energy out of a machine that is only 70 per cent efficient.

I am not even vaguely suggesting that it's time for all middle-aged folks to just sit back and wait for the final whistle. Moderate exercise is not contraindicated in those who receive a physical okay.

For example, such persons may play nine holes of golf, take a swim, ride horseback, play a set or two of tennis doubles with friends in their own age group, spend an hour in the garden, bowl, or walk.

Practically everything else — except similar activities requiring little effort — should be wiped off the slate in the daily schedule of extracurricular exertion.

Suppose we consider the simplest way of becoming fit. All you really need in the way of exercise can be accomplished at the dining table. This exercise consists of turning your head once from right to left; and again from left to right when the second portion comes around.

Such daily "exercise of your head" will keep your weight normal. And nothing else you can do will be more conducive to health and longevity. Life is not a sprint. The long race is to the lazy — and the lean.

There is a widespread misconception that it is necessary to exercise often and vigorously to reduce. Here is the case of a woman in her forties who needed help for a sprained back. It happened while she was performing reducing exercises. Somebody had told her, "Just try these exercises and eat everything you want." The more she exercised the more she gained, because her appetite became voracious.

She had to remain in bed for two weeks. She was put on a low-calorie diet. Without so much as exercising her little fingers she lost eight pounds.

Never attempt to take off weight by exercise. Probably you will never try to do so if you realize that you can walk a mile on the energy furnished by one caramel. You can climb to the top of a skyscraper on a few doughnuts with a half-dozen peanuts thrown in. You would have to walk about five miles to work off a generous portion of pie a la mode.

I know a man who often takes many more calories than

necessary at his evening meal. Then he lights a cigar and says, "I'm getting fat. I guess I'll go for a stroll and walk this off." It would require about a 20-mile "stroll" to walk off those calories.

Most persons have a tendency to gain about 15 pounds between 30 and 40 years of age. They add more poundage after 50. Exercise will *not* keep down this weight.

If you ever have the urge to exercise for your nerves, better subscribe to that tried-and-true credo: "Whenever I feel like exercising I lie down until the feeling passes."

If your doctor insists that exercise will help you, rear up on your hind legs and refuse. If he blusters, you may quote me. I'll try to catch all the brickbats he throws my way — for interfering.

EXERCISE AFTER 40? YES!*

RICHARD I. MILLER, Ed.D.

SINCE understanding is a two way path and generally truth is the compromise of antagonistic opinions, it seems proper to question some of Dr. Steincrohn's statements and bring in evidence to substantiate the belief that rational physical activity or exercise is a desirable part of living for any age.

Let us begin with one of Dr. Steincrohn's statements, "Too many Americans are exercise-mad." It is true that too much of anything may turn gold to rust. One can eat too much, sleep too much, work too much, worry too much, and exercise too much. In this sense "exercise-madness" would be harmful. However, the "bay-windows" and poor physical condition of the average middle-age American male shows no indication toward "exercise-madness." The physical strength and endurance of World War II draftees showed unexpected weaknesses. These weaknesses in strength and endurance may well have a limiting effect upon the time a man can maintain top efficiency for his daily tasks.

In the Scandinavian countries, Norway, Sweden, and Finland, middle-age participation in strenuous competitive activities is a common occurrence. As far as can be determined, this program is not the least bit harmful. However, the important consideration is whether the participant has continuously used strenuous physical activity throughout his life or whether he occasionally competes in strenuous activities. If one has continuously maintained physical activity and has a periodic health examination which indicates sound organic functioning, there is no reason why he will not physically and mentally profit from rational physical competition or exercise as long as life lasts.

Too many Americans do not use physical activity or exercise

---
* *Science Digest*, November 1950, pp. 45-47.

with discretion. Can you think of a friend who takes his physical activity in spurts? Maybe he will play 36 holes of golf on one Sunday a month or occasionally play three or four hours of tennis. As Dr. Steincrohn mentioned, this type of spurt exercising may do more harm than good. If physical activity is to be helpful, it must be regular and adapted to the individual.

Does physical exercise shorten the life span? Again it is necessary to differentiate between good and bad. The spurt of whimsical type of physical activity definitely may be harmful.

There is no proof that a regular and individually adapted program of physical activity shortens or lengthens the life span. The primary purpose of physical activity is to equip us with greater strength, endurance, and vitality to perform our daily tasks, and to offer us an opportunity for release of mental tensions. These are important contributions toward making each of us more efficient and capable in our daily tasks.

Why worry about how long we are going to live? It seems far more important that we emphasize each day's living with an eye to the future and an ear to the past. After all, length of life is measured by what a man does with the years he lives and not so much by the number of years he lives.

Quoting from Dr. Steincrohn's article, "A pleasurable feeling of relaxation should set in at about 40 years of age." Relaxation should be an important element of everyday living throughout our lives and not exclusively after 40 years. In most lines of work, the flower of success seldom blossoms before middle age. It is unlikely that a man will learn to relax after he achieves success. The responsibilities of success heavily infringe upon available time, and the stimulation of success will overshadow the importance of relaxation unless the importance of daily relaxation has been realized and practiced along the way. A hobby of some sort is an excellent way to relax. Worry is relaxation's greatest enemy. Most things we worry about are beyond our scope of influence and most of the worries within our scope of influence never happen.

Again, quoting from Dr. Steincrohn's article, "You can be healthy without crooking a little finger in exercise." In a literal sense, Dr. Steincrohn is correct because physical strength or endurance has not been found to increase resistance to disease. However, a definite line must be drawn between health and fitness. Health is medically defined as freedom from disease. Fitness may be defined as the ability to perform daily tasks without undue physical or mental fatigue.

In 1943, a distinguished group of doctors, physical educators and health specialists met in conference to establish a national policy on "The Role of Exercise in Physical Fitness." The following statement is part of their summary: "Exercise is one of the factors contributing to total fitness."

Another part of their summary stated: "Exercise should be graded according to age, capacity of the individual, and his state of training and fitness. In general, exercise should be modified in the direction of less strenuous activities after the age of 40 years."

This statement assumes that every medically approved person should have some kind of physical activity. After 40, one needs less exercise than he needed 10 or 20 years earlier, but still there is need for a regularly and rationally conducted program of physical activity. Each of us varies in his exercise tolerance much the same as our appetite and sleep requirements vary. What may be just the right amount of activity for one person may be entirely wrong for another. Each person must gauge himself according to his own exercise tolerance.

The amount of physical activity necessary for total fitness varies with occupations as well as with individuals. A manual worker needs less extracurricular physical activity than the desk worker.

The optimum amount of physical activity necessary to maintain total fitness is a highly individual matter that must be adapted to each individual, his environmental conditions, and his work.

A few additional suggestions should help in planning the contribution of exercise toward total fitness.

1) Ten to 15 minutes of exercise each day are very helpful

in the maintenance of middle-age fitness. These exercises should pay special attention to the abdominal region.

2) Some walking each day is highly recommended.

3) Do not take large doses of physical activity unless your body and mind have had systematic training and feel ready for the activity.

4) Compete against men near your own age and ability.

5) Play the game for the game's sake and the enjoyment of play.

TURN BACKWARD OH TIME . . .*

FREDERIC W. TERRIEN, Ph.D.

WHILE the figures denoting rate of population increase have changed somewhat unevenly over the past thirty years, the *proportion* of people 45 and over has marched steadily upward for a century. Though we may produce enough new people to reach the 200 million mark predicted by Dr. Louis I. Dublin for the turn of the next century, there is little likelihood that this upward trend will be reversed, because every effort of modern medicine and economics is directed toward increasing the length of life and hedging it about with protection. Life expectancy for children born today is over 70 years on the one hand; on the other, the government has hiked the Old and Survivors Insurance coverage by some 27.6 per cent with the Social Security Act Amendments of 1954.

What effect will all this have on American values, and particularly on decision-making processes and the over-all philosophic orientation of the population? Will it mean a greater conservatism — a greater tendency to move cautiously — an increased desire to judge the present by the standards of the past? Recent American writers have produced a number of works depicting the problems facing the aging businessman — *Executive Suite, Death of A Salesman,* and the TV play, *Patterns* — and, in every case, the aging protagonists found themselves not only threatened by the vitality of the young and by the changes the young brought but additionally handicapped by their own tendency to look backward for their standards of how things ought to be. Is this a universal tendency? Is there something generic about the frequent connection between age and the wistful backward look?

* *Geriatrics, 15*:3, 145-151, March 1960.

There appears to be a tendency, not limited to old men but characteristic of all men, to harken to the days of their own youth as the time when things were good and to the days when their fathers were young as a kind of golden age. The sense of the hymn which bespeaks the old time religion as being good enough for father and therefore good enough for me seems extensively to apply, if not to technological matters, at least to matters of morality and character, to wisdom, and even to physical prowess. Homer, whose storied life twenty-five centuries ago might be supposed to define the oldest good old days for the better part of Western civilization, has Nestor say:

> Come, repel
> These young men's passions. Y'are not both, put your years in one,
> So old as I. I liv'd long since, and was companion
> With men superior to you both, who yet would ever hear
> My counsels with respect. My eyes yet never witness were,
> Nor ever will be, of such men . . .

The conviction among the living that they have fallen from great estate is not new. All of mythology is based on the belief that there were giants in the earth in times past. Significantly, the great deeds of mythology never took place last year, or a generation ago, or within the memory of living man. Invariably, and by definition, they occurred so long ago that nothing remains of them but the story. Credulity, as necessary to men as food, makes anything believable if it happened far enough away in space and time.

But there must be reasons for this generalized harkening to the past for the standards of the good, the true, the beautiful, and the heroic.

In a certain sense, the life of every individual is somewhat similar to that attributed to the Garden of Eden or to that in the tale of Pandora's box. There is at first a period of innocence and relative freedom from care, during which all wants are supplied and trouble is something that is only vaguely understood and nearly always held off by someone else. It is only with the coming of adolescence and a ripening of the powers of sex and self-awareness that most young people are first introduced to the idea that life is a series of choices and decisions. The great awakening does not come with the suddenness of the eye-openings of a puppy; over a period of a relatively few years immediately preceding adolescence, there arrive and are absorbed in the growing consciousness a series of shocks which bear home the fact that the world is not the ordered place originally presented by the parents, but one full of cares outside the immediate realm of the awakening individual. A recognition of unanticipated disorder, not the least item of which is the fallibility of the parents themselves, is borne upon the newer citizen, and distinctions between his fellows which he might not have drawn, dislikes which might not have occurred to him, and thwartings of an ultimate justice he has been taught to expect, are all part of the loss of the implicit faith in the best of all possible worlds with which Western culture seeks to equip the young. Here, perhaps, are the beginnings of the feelings lumped under the cliché "insecurity." Given this and given suffering from the pain of indecision and the awareness of irregularity, a return to order is all but mandatory, even though that order be, as Freud noted, the order of the womb.

Again, youth is for most people a time of good health — indeed, it is in these days of medical wonders a time of buoyant health, when the newly-grown muscles are ready for anything, when they tire and recover, instead of tiring and aching. The health of youth, more than that of any other period of life, is assertive and positive, outgoing in the sense that it is more than a sufficiency. One does not, when young, feel simply all right; one feels like walking on the ceiling, whatever the dictates of the law of gravity. The whirlwind play of the moppet, the nervous, explosive energy of the high school boy, or the evident ability of the high school girl to study all day and dance all night appall the mature and attest to the abundance with which nature endows the young. Such a surplus means that one can, in this heyday, not only endure the ills to which the flesh is heir but strongly fight off and, for the most part, be free of them. All this is remembered, however, consciously or subconsciously, by the individual when age comes upon him, bringing with it slowing movements, awareness of chronic small aches, and the necessity of compensating for infirm muscles, fading vision, and missing teeth. If one looks back on the days of his youth as a time when things were good, who can say that such a view is not based in reality, with reference to that most important measure of value — health?

Furthermore, youth is a time of ideals, when the culture is passed on by the preceding generation pretty largely in terms, not of what *is*, but of what *ought to be*. When one is young, dreams are justified, for all of time is possessed and bent to their realization, and the future holds an incontrovertible promise that what may be wrong with the present will not be wrong with the future. Countless graduation speakers echo McCrae's cry, "To you from failing hands we throw the torch," and youth responds with less cynicism than it cares to admit. Idealism is planted in the young by dictates of cultures seeking survival and finds rich nurture in the young because it gives direction to lives which seek direction.

Such normative training permits of hero worship, since the newcomer's role must be defined. Significantly enough, the hero is generally older than the imitator and, therefore, of the generation preceding him. The youth looks forward to the time when he may be somewhat like the model — but with reference to his own life span, he must look backward in time to find him. Again, he scarcely hopes to rival his hero, and, as the hero retreats in time, he may not rival him, for the circumstances of the hero's success are never repeated exactly. What boy can now aspire to be the first man to fly the ocean alone? Youth is the time of anticipated success, when all plans are viable, and so, for the old and unsuccessful, youth becomes a kind of romantic dream of never-was, a time when the successes then hoped for in the future are now, in that realized future, attributed in reality to youth, for most of the old are unsuccessful in terms of what they hoped to be in age. If the recognition of the modesty of present success is painful for the old, they can keep some part of their dreams inviolate if they store them, to use Lowell's phrase, "safe in the hallowed quiets of the past."

The bright dreams of the barefoot boy need not, under such circumstances, be completely exposed on the altar of truth seeking.

PRIMARY ASSOCIATIONS

Powerful among the factors which give strength and validity to the philosophy of the backward look are the primary group associations of youth. These are the early relationships with the very few people who define the child's growing world to him — his family, his small playmates, and, later, his friends. Social scientists have written ably of the shaping strength of these relationships. Cooley has held that "They are primary in several senses, but chiefly in that they are fundamental in forming the social nature and ideals of the individual." MacIver has noted that "The primary group, in the form of the family, initiates us into the secrets of society . . . It is the breeding ground of our mores, the nurse of our loyalties." The essential quality of the primary group is that it is initially defining, so far as our understanding of the world is concerned. No matter what we learn and no matter how sophisticated we become, we still tend, however vestigially, to interpret what we learn through the defining frame of our primary group. It is for this reason that the psychologists emphasize the importance of the first few years of life.

The primary group associations — especially those with family and friends — are the first that the individual knows of social life, and, if he is lucky, they are the last, for these relationships are primary not only in the sense that they are first in point of time but also in the sense that they are first in point of value. The old are lonely when time inevitably reduces the number of primary associations they have made, which are by definition rare; the dying man calls for his mother and his wife, sometimes for his children or his friend of a lifetime — not for a business associate, an acquaintance, or a customer. The tragedy of Willy Loman's life as a salesman was that he mistook the casual for the primary relationships, not realizing that being "well-liked" was as tenuous as the shoeshine and the smile on which he built his career.

Because the primary group is defining of judgment for the individual, it is natural that he looks back on the attitudes with which he was equipped by that group and the experiences he shared with it as outlining that which is good — much as he looks back on his mother's cooking, whatever her culinary skills, as a kind of starting point from which to judge all he later eats. It is natural, also, that as the individual moves away from the deep satisfactions of the primary group toward the more formal and competitive secondary group, he will of necessity undergo certain major adjustments.

The secondary group — the greater world outside — is opposite the primary group on a continuum of intimacy. Here associations are formed for reasons extrinsic to the personalities of the individuals involved and rest on the goals which the people have in common or on the mutual services which they can perform. Relationships are contractual and, rather than relying for their governing on an awareness of the inner wishes of the parties in question, are controlled by rules, depending on outside agencies for their enforcement. Where, in the primary group, all associations are intimate, enduring, and predictable, rooted in what Davis calls an "inclusive knowledge" of the other parties, the associations of the secondary group are formal, largely transitory, and much less predictable. The satisfactions of the first lie in an intimate knowledge of the personalities of all involved; the satisfactions of the second lie largely in the effectiveness with which the individual may operate to his own advantage or to the attainment of some fixed goal outside himself.

The person who has spent a number of reasonably satisfactory years in the primary group — which is the lot of most people — may find that the transfer of his major activities to the larger and more impersonal sphere of the secondary group is difficult of adjustment. Some persons never satisfactorily cross the line and wander through what they feel is an increasingly hostile world of secondary groups, seeking the reward of a primary which is not, by definition, to be found therein. At best, it comes as a shock to the most stable of individuals to find that, when he leaves the primary group for more formal and fleeting associations, he cannot transfer the same values to the larger entity. Whatever his willingness to move forward to maturity, he will be disappointed with the ethics of the more competitive and impersonal secondary group. He will inevitably look back on his early days and say to himself that "things like this never used to happen." As far as he himself is concerned, he is right. The values of the competitive world are not those of the primary group, and it is a shock to learn this truth. But the individual is only beginning to learn about the world; it is *his* ideas that are being forcibly revised, not necessarily the values of society. Few are aware that it is themselves who have changed, becoming more sentient, and not the world which has changed, heading toward evil and destruction.

It is easy enough, in any age, to find concrete evidence that the society is decaying, but the individual who becomes convinced that this process obtains seldom judges the situation in terms of the needs of the world at the time. He is aware of change but, by and large, not sufficiently so to be aware also of the reasons for change; consequently, in order to satisfy his need for explanations, he retreats to make his judgments from a point where he may be sure of his definitions, and that point is the ethos of his primary group.

It is clear that the central idea involved is this idea of *social change* and the resistance of men to this change. It is difficult to make a value judgment as to whether men should or should not resist change. We make what La Piere calls a "function judgment" and analyze a particular piece of resistance to change for its direct utility to society, but we cannot make a value judgment on the whole item of resistance to change. It is possible only to observe that resistance to change is as necessary to the continuance of society as is advocacy of change. If change were continuous and rapid, society would be in a kind of dynamic chaos; if change never occurred — which, of course, is unthinkable — society would be in a condition so static as to make impossible the continuing life of human beings, who are themselves different from each other, and therefore the source of change.

REASONS FOR RESISTANCE TO CHANGE

But, to concentrate on the reasons that men resist change, let us examine the oft-quoted, much studied, frequently maligned but never identified average man. He spends a minimum of some sixteen years, by law, learning to live in the culture of this country, and then puts in another thirty getting himself into a position where he has a few of the products of that culture which he may call his own and, so calling, feel that he is "successful." By the time he reaches middle age, he has managed to master his situation so that he is, if not on top of the world, at least on the upper slope of the globe. So far as his unkept monthly resolutions to budget himself will permit, he is solvent. He has a home, a wife, two or three children, a car, and a van load of artifacts, such as a refrigerator, stove, radio, furniture, an extra suit, and some fishing tackle. In addition, he has managed to put by enough each month to give him a few thousand dollars worth of life insurance. The average man has about *these* things and very little more, and it has taken him something more than half his life to lay hands on them.

Now let us suppose that a few changes be introduced. The form of government is altered, our man is forced out of his job, the currency is devaluated, or he is forbidden to own or accumulate property. What will happen? The average man will resist these drastic changes with everything in his power for the simple reason that he is conscious of the work he has done to secure what he has, and he knows that he does not have the time to start over again. He has made his major effort in life; he has, with more or less success, adjusted to one way of living; he will have neither the time nor the energy to make another such adjustment. One time around is enough.

Many men have faced complete reversals and have come out of the experience better off than they were originally. This is particularly true in the cases of some of the refugees who fled the pogroms of Europe to make striking successes in this country — but these are not average histories. The truer picture of the typical person who experienced a pogrom is that of a tired, desperate figure loaded with a sack of useless pots and blankets, carrying a dying child, staggering down the road to oblivion.

Change is a function of the unknown, and the unknown, in the human as well as in the animal world, is fraught with the potentiality of harm. Change may benefit some members of a society, but it will just as surely harm others, and everybody, *everybody* has a vested interest in the *status quo*. The *status quo* may be grossly unfair and inimical to a certain class of people, as most certainly the *status quo* of Czarist Russia was inimical to the peasants, but even they resisted drastic change because they had a stake in things as they were. This stake was not in property, not in comfort, not in justice, not in opportunity — it was rather in *familiarity* with things as they were then done. done.

It is not true that you cannot teach an old dog new tricks, but the new tricks constitute an adjustment for the old dog which is difficult for him to make. Among human beings, every change calls for a readjustment, every readjustment means a new tension, and every new tension brings about a new set of neural patterns — or, if you will, an additional hardening of the arteries. All people find, sooner or later, that there is a limit to this process. One day they must resist time and its hand-maiden, change, lest the world be totally unfamiliar.

Finally, there is the matter of mutual exclusiveness of the directions in which a man may look — a matter which very likely does as much to explain the viability of the backward look as does any other factor. The rabbit, a creature whose defense against the hostile forces of nature lies in flight, is so constructed that he can look in two directions at once — forward and backward. Man is less gifted in this respect. His stereoscopic vision is forever committed to one direction at a time. A choice must be made on the physical level, and apparently the same choice is made on the philosophic level. In both cases, these choices seem to be mutually exclusive.

The man who commits his philosophic vision primarily to the

front is made continually aware of the troubles of the present
and must perforce ponder the imaginable difficulties of the
future, often more forbidding because they lie in that "undis-
cover'd country" whose bourne only speculation describes. The
task of facing up to the steadily unreeling panorama of the
present and of out-guessing the potentialities of the future is
one which is easy for youth, because youth, backed against
the lower end of the continuum of life, has nowhere to look but
ahead. But, when a good part of life has been lived, and a
measure of life's satisfactions and rewards have been achieved
in a framework understood and, to a certain extent, mastered,
there is room for a choice in the direction in which one may
face. Indeed, for the old, the backward look covers the greatest
range of possible experience; the uneasy eye of age detects all
too clearly the upper end of the continuum of life, where the
wall, for this carnal sphere, is as blank as that at the start.

Again, if a man is looking backward, he cannot, of physical
and philosophic necessity, look forward at the same time. By
concentrating on what has gone before, he is relieved of the
grim task of concentrating either on a changing present or on a
future whereof he will not be around to exert control. The
present is only barely within his authority; the future — as he
knows well enough — belongs to others.

There is small comfort in the words of Macaulay, who said
that "no man who is correctly informed as to the past, will be
disposed to take a morose or desponding view of the present,"
for the present, in its fleeting passage, speeds a future which
can include only the memory of the greatest captains and the
greatest kings. The old must heed the ancient warning, *carpe
diem*, for the day they knew best slips from their fingers. The
choice of the backward look, then, is eminently reasonable in
that it lends meaningful support to the universal will to survive.

If the lonely and fragile human ego is to endure in a world
of change, it must cling in its value-seeking to a time when it
was master of that change. These thoughts are part of each
individual's definition of life. Some idea of their strength and

their necessity may perhaps be gained from the recent words of one who for a generation has been the hottest of hot jazz men — Louis Armstrong. Said he, "The new cats around now, they ain't provin' nothin'."

A SOUND APPROACH TO MIDDLE AGE[*]

ALBERT J. LEVINE, Ph.D.

THE middle years, as a span of life, suffer from statistical vagueness. The person approaching middle age strives to delay its advent until the age of 40. The admittedly middle-aged persons insists on fixing its upper limit at 60. In an average life of 70 years, the span from 36 to 55 would be nearer a middle allocation than 40 to 60.

In terms of biologic and psychologic changes, middle life may be marked off from adulthood and later maturity, but it is not susceptible to sharp demarcation, for each stage of life merges imperceptibly into the next.

Since neither the calendar nor the statistician can set off sharply the middle-aged group from the rest of the maturing population, we have to resort to certain signs that body and mind are becoming less responsive to the demands of life, and that, in fighting life's battles, the weapons are growing duller and the opponent's sharper.

EMOTIONAL REACTIONS TO AGING

The signs of aging are easy to read, but those who read differ greatly in awareness. Some persons note their presence but insist that they are warning signs, cautionary amber lights. They insist that all that is needed is a little dieting, occasional rest periods, and an assortment of vitamin pills. In this group belong the practitioners of strenuous living who operate on the premise that man can live a free-wheeling existence up to age 35.

Other persons react with alarm to the signs of aging. Like drivers suddenly faced with a red light, they slam on their men-

* *Geriatrics*, 12:625-626, October 1957.

tal brakes to avert disaster. Their superheated emotions accomplish two things: 1) they dim the threat of the red danger signal long enough to restore emotional calm, and 2) they set in motion a series of rationalizations to alleviate the painful situation. The threat is met with denial, "I am still as good as ever: I never felt better." When denial continues to collide with facts, rationalization takes over, running the gamut from self-deception to concealment. "It's only lack of practice that is slowing up my tennis game." "Gray hair? It makes me look dignified!"

As to concealment, nature is always resorting to it in its use of protective coloration. By its dispensation, the impact of aging can be cushioned by a simulated youthfulness. If men were not so sensitive to the gibes of the other sex, they would openly resort to the beautician. This feeling does not preclude the use of such age-erasing devices as toupees, hair bleaching, and face lifting.

While men pretend to sanction their use on vocational grounds only, women have had no such scruples. By keeping their age stationary, their weight immobile, their complexions clear, and their smiles warm, they find it easy to draw the admiration of males and to hold the affections of their mates. The bloom of youth has faded, but the counterfeit freshness that has succeeded it is enhanced by the indefinable beautifier called maturity.

WHY PHILOSOPHY FALLS SHORT

However, this escape from aging into the haven of continued youthfulness does not rid one of the fear of growing old. By the time the 40's have rolled around, the feeling deepens that no philosophy of life, however profound or esoteric, can avail against the growing disillusionments brought by the practical exigencies and vulgarities of life.

Nor can one find in philosophy solace from the increasing opaqueness of the senses and the cooling of the passions, for life is lived largely on the practical and physical planes. "Outrageous fortune" continues to hurl its "slings and arrows," and, whenever the barbs strike, they cause pain that no philosophy can entirely assuage.

If philosophy proves inadequate as a substitute for physical well-being, it is equally unsatisfactory as a compensatory preoccupation. There are too many diverse systems clamoring for recognition and too many protagonists who depend more on window dressing and high pressure salesmanship than on reasoning.

With the loss of philosophic crutches and acceleration, other fears arise, the foremost of which is the fear of senility. There is something indecent in senile degeneration that offends the esthetic sense. Many persons cannot become reconciled to the inevitableness of death, and the spectacle of slow dissolution offends their concept of the dignity of man.

THE PSYCHOLOGIC APPROACH

It is true that the irrational fears that beset the aging process die hard. Yet one can resolve to look upon the face of age and learn to live with it. To implement the resolve, ways must be found to change one's mode of living. Habits and attitudes are not easily altered. Here the cooperative endeavors of family and friends have a salutary effect. That of a professional trained in the science of geriatrics would be incalculably more effective.

The reference is to the geriatrician. He is a new type of family physician. He is not a jack-of-all-trades specialist in the sense that he supersedes him. He is concerned with the patient's medical history, noting each malady with the thoroughness of a specialist. But whereas the specialist dissects the patient's individual organ impairment, the geriatrician reassembles him into a dynamic whole.

Properly conceived, the adjustive measures of aging need not be painful or irksome. They do not need to be the adjustment of capitulation, the surrender to a philosophy of resignation. Rather they are the adjustment of accommodation. They may involve as little effort as is expended in shortening one's stride to keep up with a slow-gaited companion, or the economizing of energy described by one middle-aged woman who announced,

"I now try to pick up as many things as possible in one bending."

Fortunately, many persons view the danger signals of aging without alarm. They view the advent of the middle years as the beginning of a new life cycle. Although it is sharply transitional, they feel confident in their ability to make the necessary adjustment. To them, middle age doesn't signal the Pitkinian renascence or the Oslerian recession. Life simply changes its tempo and rhythm. It has its deficits and compensations.

What the mind loses in alertness, it makes up for it in the assurance of reflective thinking. If the muscles grow sensitive to fatigue, they learn to respond more selectively to stimuli. If the bodily functions show signs of impairment, they flash intermittently the amber lights of caution. And if the fires of passions are being damped, one comes to prize the release from their tyrannical domination.

LIFE COURSE IN MIDDLE AGE*

J. S. SLOTKIN, Ph.D.

ONE significant way of viewing the life of an individual is in relation to what has been termed his "life course." This has two components: life goal and career. Life goals are those aims which have highest value, can be attained only after a relatively protracted series of activities, and become the person's reason for existence. The series of activities engaged in to achieve these goals constitute a career. The life goals give purpose and meaning to one's life; the career directs and organizes life.[1]

Charlotte Bühler and her associates have found that in Western society people go through a regular sequence of five stages in their life course.[2] The first is the exploratory stage of youth (beginning at an average age of 17), in which the individual tentatively tries out various life courses. The second is the selective stage of maturity (beginning at an average age of 28), in which the individual definitely decides upon specific life goals and channelizes his activities accordingly into a particular career. The third is the testing stage of early middle age (beginning at an average age of 43); it is a period in which the individual examines his career to determine the extent to which he has achieved his life goals and the degree to which he has obtained the gratifications he hoped to gain from his life course.

---

* *Social Forces,* 33:171-177, December 1954.

1. J. S. Slotkin: *Personality Development.* New York, Harper, 1952, pp. 225-233.
2. Charlotte Bühler: *Der menschliche Lebenslauf als psychologisches Problem.* Leipzig, Hirzel, 1933, and "The Curve of Life as Studied in Biographies," *Journal of Applied Psychology,* 19 (1935), pp. 405-409; E. Frenkel: "Studies in Biographical Psychology," *Character and Personality,* 5 (1936) pp. 1-34.

The fourth stage is that of indulgence in later middle age (beginning at an average of 48); the individual concentrates on achieving the maximum gratification from what remains of vigorous life. The fifth is the completion stage of old age (beginning at an average age of 64); in it the individual looks back on his life, lives on past accomplishment, and begins to finish off his life course.

A good deal of work is being done on the first two stages by students of adolescence and early maturity and on the last stage by students of old age, but relatively little scientific research has been undertaken on the third and fourth stages of middle age.[3] The importance of the subject — the fact that middle age presents a problem to Americans — is indicated by the circumstance that a book like *Life Begins at Forty*[4] has been a best seller. The present paper, therefore, deals with the results of a study of the life course in middle age (Bühler's third and fourth stages). We will start with a consideration of the adjustment made by Americans.

The third or testing stage is one in which the individual compares his level of achievement with his level of aspiration. On this basis he may decide he is a failure, inconclusive, partially successful, or successful.

Failures are of two types, the acknowledged and the grandoise.

The acknowledged failure is an individual who, when going through the testing stage, decides that he has not achieved to any appreciable degree the life goals toward which he aspires and that neither his abilities nor the conditions confronting him will ever permit him to do so. This judgment is either objectively warranted or made because of a psychotic depression. The result is that the failure feels that he has pursued his life course in vain, and his reason for existence disappears. Few people have the courage to acknowledge failure, and so this adjustment is relatively rare. Some, in despair, try to escape;

---

3. For example, G. L. Elliott: *Women after Forty.* New York, Henry Holt, 1936.
4. W. B. Pitkin: *Life Begins at Forty.* New York, McGraw-Hill, 1932.

the extreme adjustment in this case is suicide.[5] Others develop a stoic outlook. Most find it comforting to seek another purpose in life, reverting to the exploratory and selective stages in order to find a new life course which, it is hoped, will finally lead to success.

> I am a single woman and forty. . . . I know, like scores of other women, what I need in order to live. To me life is a trinity of needs—money, a mission, and a man. At twenty there was a possibility that I might find all three. At forty I haven't even a sporting chance at any of them. I find myself doomed to exist on makeshifts—a salary, a job, and other women's husbands. And no matter how sublime the courage she feigns, no woman has ever lived the more abundant life on substitutions. What scope is there at forty for the satisfying of these needs? . . . At forty, one is able to develop a protective stoicism—thank God for that! . . . A cynicism is now mine that is not despair. It is rather the virtue of a calm courage retained by one disappointed in life and the world.[6]

Another woman in the same predicament chose to escape. She remarked, "I'm on the way to becoming the best chronic alcoholic you ever saw."

The grandoise failure also decides that he has not achieved to any appreciable degree the life goals toward which he aspires. But he has a paranoid lack of insight into his own limited abilities or the unfavorable conditions in which he finds himself. Such a person becomes embittered. He is envious of those who do succeed; he feels unappreciated. A case in point is a mediocre painter who still strives to become recognized as a genius. He spends most of his time gossiping to others about his successful competitors and complaining of the machinations of art dealers who prevent him from achieving the success he deserves.

The inconclusive individual feels that there is still some chance he will eventually achieve his original life goals, though they continue to elude him. This seems to be the commonest adjust-

---

5. M. von Andics: *Suicide and the Meaning of Life.* London, Hodge, 1947.
6. Anonymous: "Life Ends at Forty." *Forum,* 91 (1934), pp. 202-207.

ment. For it is the easiest one to make; all it requires is that the person stay on his habitual life course. Actually, a very small proportion of Americans ever achieve the life goals to which they originally aspired. But the inconclusive individual finds it convenient to ignore the fact that the odds are against him; it is more comfortable to continue as he has in the past. This type is exemplified in our contemporary literature by Willy Loman, who, after a hitherto unsuccessful career as salesman for thirty-six years, can still say, "Oh, I'll knock 'em dead next week. I'll go to Hartford. I'm very well liked in Hartford."[7]

The partial success is an individual who comes to realize that his own abilities are too limited or conditions too unfavorable for him to achieve completely his original life goals. He then lowers his level of aspiration until it becomes more commensurate with what he deems to be a possible level of achievement; for what now seems to him grandiose original life goals, he substitutes more modest and realistic ones. In order that this adjustment take place, the person has to be able to evaluate objectively both his own limited talents and/or the adverse conditions confronting him. The adjustment also requires that during the testing period he feels that he has already substantially advanced in his life course, so that the modified life goals deemed achievable bear some significant relation to the life goals originally aspired to. The period of readjustment to reduced life goals is difficult and often agonizing, for it involves a revaluation and diminution of one's conception of himself and his ego ideal. It is for this reason that one man said "I'm afraid to" engage in any conscious testing; unconsciously he suspected that he would have to accommodate himself to partial success with all that it implies. But such an adjustment also has its reward; the person can now enjoy modest satisfaction in achieving attainable, if limited, life goals. An example of the partially successful is found in the comments of an orchestra musician:

7. A. Miller: *Death of a Salesman*. New York, Bantam, 1951, p. 34.

There is hardly a member of the Philharmonic who did not aspire at one time to become a virtuoso. My own dream was to conduct opera. Most of us have had to give up aspirations of that kind because of the time and expense involved. [Notice that he attributes failure to unfavorable conditions and not to limited talent. It is less damaging to one's conception of himself!] Faced with the problem of making a living, we did the next best thing for ourselves artistically—we took jobs with the Philharmonic-Symphony. Eventually all of us become realistic enough to know that we will never reach the pinnacle. We become reconciled to our status. After that it becomes a matter of trying to advance to the first desk in our section. That is only a matter of prestige—it does not affect our salaries—but it helps our egos a bit.[8]

Success are of two types, the satisfied and the dissatisfied. The satisfied success is one who, during the testing period, deems that he has achieved his original life goals and believes that these goals are gratifying. This occurs when he finds he originally had made a valid judgment about the kinds of goals which would satisfy him. He then contentedly continues on his original life course during the fourth stage. A case in point is found in the following remarks of a humanistic scholar:

I could have been to a certain extent a writer. . . . And in my general circle, to be a university professor . . . to be a scholar of something . . . was certainly one of the highest things you could reach . . . Well, I realized I could never really make a living as a writer . . . regardless of how good or how bad I would be. And scholarship interested me very much; I would never have wanted to give that up. So what I wanted to be was a professor in the university . . . I wanted to pursue the academic career. I wanted to do as much work as humanly possible in my own way; to be as unbothered by rules and regulations as possible, and . . . to have the means to pursue this existence without having to look too much to the right and the left. And, this, more or less, I got . . .

8. G. Imparato: "A Fifth Viola's View of an Orchestra." *New York Times,* December 19, 1949, Section 6, p. 19.

[He is now one of the most distinguished scholars in his field.] In terms of having pre-formed the way in which the next thirty years the people will look upon things . . . [in my field], they may not know it, but . . . this they have all from me . . . Of course, you cannot help being pleased to a certain extent. Also, it gives you possibilities for doing further things. I mean, in this world of ours, prestige is a wonderful key . . . Quite a few of the things which I am doing now, I could never have done without that, apart from my intellectual abilities or disabilities. This is true. But usually you are not aware of it. Just imagine you are a train, and you are going to San Francisco or somewhere, but you do not know where you are going. All right. You suddenly find your self in the height of the Rockies, and it is really nice that you got there. But you have no time to think about this, because your problem is: Will you be able to be at six o'clock in — I don't know — there or there? . . . I suppose that my work, rather than my career, is probably the most important element for me. So that this is why I'm so dreadfully dependent on the continuance of my productivity . . . There is still a lot to be said and a lot to be done, because, after all, ours is a cumulative business . . .

It's pleasant work. I like that kind of thing . . . It's a gracious way of living . . . You have no boss. You arrange your time with very small concessions to others. Your surroundings are nice. The people you are thrown with are of the better kind. You live in the world of ideas, but not so far removed from reality. On the contrary, it gives you an access to reality which the so-called man of affairs, apart from the people who are really tops, do not have. I mean, the lack of insight of, say, the average businessman or employee into the workings of life — as compared to us, it is pitiful . . . Also, it gives us a certain detachment and a distance to judge the regularities [and] irregularities, the particular and the general, and so on, which makes living a — well, perhaps not necessarily a joy, but a somewhat more intense and worthwhile experience than it would be otherwise . . . And then . . . there is simply a certain affinity between the way I am made and the things I do . . . Why do I work? Just because it's fun. I like the idea of sitting down and working . . .

> For my happiness and my feeling of justification of my being
> on this earth is somehow tied up with this. Otherwise, I
> think the regularity of having to shave every morning, and
> so forth, would not be bearable.

The dissatisfied success also decides that he has achieved his original life goals but finds that dominant desires still remain ungratified. This occurs when he finds he originally made an invalid judgment about the kinds of goals which would satisfy him, or neurotic inner conflicts prevent him from obtaining the gratification objectively available to him. Three alternatives are open to the dissatisfied success.

The first is escape, characteristically taking the form of suicide.[9] If he has found it difficult to pursue his life course and discovers that after long and arduous exertion the life goals are ashes in his mouth, he tends to become disillusioned. And if, at the same time, he participates in a disorganized culture having no fixed value system, he becomes skeptical of the worth of any life goals whatever. It was stated at the beginning of this paper that life goals give purpose and meaning to life and that a career directs and organizes life. Now, without further life goals, the individual finds his life purposeless and meaningless; without a further career, his life seems random and unorganized. Therefore he feels that any more struggle as severe as that which he has gone through previously is not worth the effort. One man contemplating suicide summed it up in these words, "It's too much trouble to live."

The second alternative of the dissatisfied success is to become a hedonist and seek relatively immediate gratifications in the fourth stage. This adjustment occurs when the individual has found it relatively easy to pursue his life course, and participates in a disorganized culture whose value system has broken down. His disillusionment with his previous life course, and the absence of an accepted system of social values, makes him doubt whether any goals are worth protracted effort. Ecclesiastes presents the classic exposition of this viewpoint:

---

9. M. von Andics, *op. cit.*

I considered all that my hands had done and the toil I had spent in doing it, and behold, all was vanity and striving after wind, and there was nothing to be gained under the sun. . . . Behold, what I have seen to be good and to be fitting is to eat and drink and find enjoyment in all the toil with which one toils under the sun the few days of his life.[10]

The third alternative of the dissatisfied success is to choose a new life course, selecting new life goals and starting a new career in the fourth stage. This adjustment is made by the individual who participates in an organized culture having an established value system. Consequently he does not question the validity of the system of social values and related life goals; instead, he believes that he made a mistake in choosing his original life goals, which now have proven unsuitable for him personally. Therefore he reverts to the exploratory and selective stages: first experimenting with a variety of different life goals, and then choosing new specific goals which he hopes will give him the satisfactions he desires.

I felt that I should like to have my life accomplish certain goals. First and probably foremost, I wanted to — quote — contribute to society, benefit humanity, leave my droppings on the sands of time; in some way leave the world a better place by virtue of my efforts than it had been when I arrived on the scene. I wanted to make sure that my children would not go through all of the unnecessary convolutions that I had gone through. . . . Now, there were secondary goals. I should have liked to have achieved that contribution in the realm of accepted and recognized effort, if not widely and universally accepted, at least accepted by those constituting a smaller circle whose esteem I would value. I should like the effort to be one which would financially remunerate me to an extent that I would not know insecurity, poverty; to the extent that I could support a family and educate my children. But the major focal point was to sacrifice something in order to achieve this contribution. I felt, at that time, that anyone could achieve

10. *Holy Bible*, Revised Standard Version. New York, Nelson, 1952. Ecclesiastes, 5: 2.11, 5.18.

the secondary goals of esteem and respect by some group in society and financial gain. Anyone could achieve those things, ignoring the first larger goal, because that then was in the realm of conventional effort — going into business or into various profit making enterprises. Mine was finding this very unique — well, not very unique, but difficultly achieved — spot in which I could do no one harm, yet rather do society good and still make a living at it. . . .

[He took a technical position in a government agency.] It certainly represented my not selling my mind to the highest bidder for his use in the accumulating of gain. It was a socially useful job. It was not a particularly thrilling job, in the sense that one's findings were immediately put to a social use; but there was the realization that over the long period of time the building blocks which we made at C — [the government agency] — namely, the data that we collected and processed — these building blocks would be the basic material out of which the structures of the future would be raised; the basic findings of what needed remedial measures were our findings. . . . My name would be one of a number of names in these imperishable C — volumes which would be on the shelves of every library in the world. . . . I was chief of a unit. I was considered management. I participated in conferences and consultations. . . . I would say that, in my own mind, and apparently in the minds of my friends and colleagues, I had achieved a position as honorable as that of a professor on a campus. The pay scales were somewhat commensurate. My security was greater. I was doing honorable work, necessary work. And with each passing year, I was becoming more and more the authority in my little subject matter. . . . If the statement involves only the objective factors of the situation. . . . I achieved — in a rather remarkable fashion, it seems to me — the goals that I had set for myself in my more impressionable and idealistic youth.

But if getting away from the mere, "These are the facts I wanted to achieve, and these are the facts I achieved" — if getting away from that is permissible . . . although I had verbalized and articulated goals which sounded pleasing to me and to those to whom I enunciated them . . . . apparently there were needs or desires in me that these — conventional and acceptable to most of those about me — rewards were not satisfying. . . . My complaints apparently were those that I could not, and even now I am not too well able to, articulate. I was bored. Deep down inside, somewhere. . . . Finally, I resigned. . . .

I decided somewhere along the line — or at least I rationalized somewhere along the line in weariness — that all I would ask of life was the chance to have a job, to do it fairly well, and get paid for it to an extent that I could support my family. The idealism, the extra energy, all of those things drifted out of the picture. . . . I should like to provide for my kids; I should like to leave them somewhat better off than I was left. Beyond that, the larger part of society will have to get along without my contribution. I don't want to harm society, but I have all I can do to take care of my own immediate family. . . . I said almost in jest, when I was coming here from Washington, that I would do anything that would pay off quickly. I was tired of spending year after year making both ends meet. I had lost some large measure of idealism, and I was ready to behave in what was to me a more unprincipled fashion. I would have opened a liquor store, I said, if it would guarantee me a good livelihood. I would even — this was jocular and to friends — I would even pimp if it would pay off. At this point every measure of idealism, I think, is out of the picture — to the extent that I would deliberately expend effort in the direction of the idealistic goals.

The middle age adjustments described above are found in the United States and can be shown to depend upon the nature of our culture. Two cultural factors stand out. In the first place, our social organization is mobile so that more individuals aspire to life goals which will improve their class position. In such cases the pursuit of the chosen life course involves a good deal of conscious effort; the individual is constantly aware of the great amount of time and energy he has invested in his career. Consequently, it is a traumatic experience for him to find that he cannot achieve the life goals he has aspired to, or — if he does achieve them — that they do not satisfy him. In the second place, our value system and related goals are such that they can be achieved early in life, so that a testing stage is meaningful, logically succeeded by an indulgence stage. For instance, it is possible for a businessman to become a millionaire or an academician to become a professor while he still has half his productive life before him. Indeed, in some cases the life goals can be achieved only in youth; then the problem arises of what to do with the rest of one's vigorous life — choosing a new life course or living on memories of past accomplishments. Thus, in our society the goal of most women is sexual attractiveness; according to our customary ideal of youthful beauty this goal is achieved by women from their late teens to early twenties.

By contrast, in a stratified society the roles, and therefore the life course, of an individual tend to be ascribed to him by virtue of the social stratum in which he is born. His life course therefore seems to be the natural way of life; he is simultaneously living in the manner expected of him and pursuing his life course. Little conscious effort is involved, and it is customary for him to achieve the life goals to which he aspires. If it so happens that those goals do not satisfy him when achieved, there is a customary alternative career open to him. This was true in the traditional European and Hindu cultures. The individual's life course depended upon his stratum or caste respectively, and if he became a dissatisfied success he could isolate himself from the secular world by becoming a monk.

In regard to the second point, testing and its consequences do not usually arise in cultures where the life goals can only be achieved late in life. In such societies the individual continues to pursue his life goals until death or until he is so old that he is ready to finish with life. Thus, among the Menomini Indians the explicit life goals are living to old age and having grandchildren. Another life goal is implicit: the group is gerontocratic, and the longer one lives the more experience and consequent wisdom he is supposed to possess. Therefore the older one is, the more status and influence he has. It is significant that among the Menomini I found none of the problems of middle age which have been discussed in reference to our own society. All of the middle-aged people interviewed considered the possibility of achieving their life goals so far in the future it never occurred to them to go through a testing period even when asked to evaluate their life courses. In terms of the classification given earlier, all middle-aged Menomini are of the inconclusive type.

Even becoming successful and maintaining that success are particularly difficult in our society. In most cultures the individual seeks a fixed life goal. For example, he may want to be a movie actor — a position which, when achieved, he can relax and enjoy. By contrast, the American characteristically tends to seek relative life goals, to obtain a certain position in respect to others. He must become a movie *star,* one of the most popular of all movie actors. The great social mobility in our society, plus its competitiveness, means that even if one does achieve shifting life goals, there is in addition a constant and conscious struggle to maintain that success relative to others. Both these aspects of our success pattern are stereotyped in the phrase, "keeping up with the Joneses." A good deal has been written on this subject in regard to business, so I will give an example from academic life instead. The humanistic scholar mentioned earlier makes a neat contrast between his situation in this country and what it would have been if he had remained in Europe.

> . . . the awkwardness — the ambivalence of our future which lies in being successful in America. I mean, if I had been reasonably successful in my profession in Europe, in the old Europe at least, I would have been given some title, or some badge, or something, and be left alone unless I had tried to get into public life or so. Here, as you know, the only way in which a success really expresses itself is that one is being saddled with more and more responsibilities, and that it is very difficult to move out because one, by saying "no" all the time, undercuts one's range too much. . . . In general, the development of American scholarship into sort of a very aristocratic club — that is to say, that in each field three or four people are accepted, more or less, as uncrowned bosses; and the rest is there, too — makes for harder concentration of responsibilities on the individuals on top, and this in turn makes it very difficult to realize all one wants to realize . . . I mean there is some sort of a mechanism

which grinds you to bits. It is almost literally traceable, that
every year another ten or twelve percent has been added to
my load; which does not necessarily mean that every year
I've done ten to twelve percent better work. . . . At best,
in 1957 can I get to this and this? Also, I shall not be able
to resist the temptation to apply for this particular money.
I'm thinking of something specific which will cover me up
for another — blanket me, as it were — for another three years;
so that will be 1960. . . Who knows what will happen? There
is a certain limit.

The informant contrasts the difficulties of achieving and maintaining success in the United States and Europe. The difference
is even more marked when we compare the Americans and the
Menomini. The latter taboo competition. All members of the
group are supposed to be on a par; the cliche used, "No one is
better than anyone else." Actually subtle forms of unconscious
competition do occur,[11] but ostensibly the life goals of the
Menomini are fixed and rather easy to obtain and enjoy (old
age and grandchildren). There is no conscious striving to achieve
and maintain success because of the existence of relative life
goals.

The last few paragraphs have asserted that the problem of
making these adjustments arises in certain cultures only. Next I
want to argue that, once the adjustments are made, difficulties
may arise because of cultural factors. This can be illustrated by
examining the occupational readjustments made by the dissatisfied successes. (Of course we need only consider the last
two of their alternatives; if they choose suicide that finishes the
matter.)

In our own society, people with unskilled or semi-skilled jobs
do not have much trouble changing occupations. Thus, a clerk
in an office finally decided that a poorly paid white-collar job
was not as gratifying as better paid factory work; it was relatively easy for him to make the change. It is in the most highly
skilled trades and professions that the difficulties occur. A man

---

11. J. S. Slotkin: "Social Psychiatry of a Menomini Community." *Journal of
Abnormal and Social Psychology, 48* (1953), pp. 10-16.

who has spent half of his life in a complex and specialized occupation has developed habits and a related conception of himself which limit the occupational changes available to him and make it difficult for him to readjust to marked changes in occupation. For example, in a case previously given, the man who had been a technical specialist in a government agency could not obtain the kind of technical job he desired in private industry, and he could not conceive of himself in the role of businessman.

> I must recognize certain limitations within myself as well as within the world around. I am not the entrepreneur type. I am what a friend of mine in private industry has called "depression scarred." The search for money cannot involve the risk type of approach. I will take less, and a good deal less. I mean a "less" which will enable me to live comfortably and sacrifice the peaks if I can be sure the troughs won't be there. . . . [He has found it difficult to obtain a suitable position.] The government experience is transferable nowhere else in the world, except in part. I became a specialist in something that is done nowhere except in government, and nowhere else in government than in C — [the agency for which he worked]. Only part of that knowledge is transferable, a part which is a common denominator of everyone's training in the general field. Why should they take me, at my age, when they can get someone fifteen or twenty years younger?

Another case is of a scientist who writes:

> I've virtually finished all the large scale research projects I planned at the beginning of my career. I have enough ideas to continue in the same way for the rest of my life, but by now I'm bored with this kind of research. I'm looking for something new. For a while I tried just loafing, but I find I need the stimulus of creative research activity in order to make life interesting for me. My tastes and habits have become molded by my way of life, so that I prefer academic life to industry or government. This means that my alternatives are limited to new kinds of academic research. I can't engage in wholly new areas of research in related fields which interest me, because I don't have the training necessary and it would

take too long to obtain it. So all that seems open to me is
is to look around for slightly different research problems, to
be attacked from slightly different points of view. This is what
I've been doing recently.

These problems of choosing new occupations among the highly
skilled occur only in complex cultures with especially developed
division of labor. In most cultures readjustment is no more
difficult than for the unskilled or semi-skilled workers in our
own society.

The conclusion I wish to draw from this study is that the
problems of middle age, like those of adolescence,[12] are not
intrinsic to the phase of life but rather a consequence of certain
cultural conditions.

12. Margaret Mead: *Coming of Age in Samoa*. New York, Morrow, 1939, part 1.

FACTORS ASSOCIATED WITH THE LIFE SATISFACTION OF MIDDLE-CLASS, MIDDLE-AGED PERSONS*‡

ARNOLD M. ROSE, Ph.D.

THE different central roles of middle-class men and women in our society — that of breadwinning for men and home-making and childrearing for women — affect other aspects of their lives, so that there are several ways in which the life patterns of middle-class men and women differ. One important difference occurs when they reach middle age: a typical male carries on his occupation as usual and may have new responsibilities associated with it, whereas a woman finds that her children have grown up and are leaving home and that her home-making function is reduced. Often she has not prepared herself for a drastic change in central role, especially when the culture does not expect her to assume specific new roles.[1] We therefore hypothesize that there will be differences in the factors affecting life satisfaction of middle-class men and women as they enter middle age.[2] More specifically, we hypothesize that the differences in factors associated with life satisfaction between the sexes will reflect the need for women to find a new central role as their role as homemaker necessarily declines.

* Grateful acknowledgment is made to the Graduate School of the University of Minnesota and to the Rockefeller Foundation for support of the study from which this paper reports some of the findings.

‡ Marriage & Family Living. Feb. 1955, pp. 15-19.

1. Arnold M. Rose: "Adequacy of Women's Expectations for Adult Roles." Social Forces, 30: 69-77, October, 1951.

2. We here operationally define the onset of middle age not in terms of years but in terms of their children's reaching the age of independence. We emphasize the middle class because a large proportion of lower-class women are expected, or find it necessary, to assume or carry on a paid job, and a large proportion of upper-class women to carry on community and entertainment responsibilities (in addition, upper-class women have the income to help them occupy their increase in leisure).

To test this hypothesis we asked students in two sociology classes at the University of Minnesota during 1952-3 to send or take home questionnaries for their parents to fill out. In 208 cases, both the father and the mother returned completed questionnaires; this was about 50 per cent of the questionnaires distributed. In the other half of the cases, one or both parents were either dead or incapacitated, unwilling to fill out the four-page questionnaire, or the student said that one or both parents was inaccessible or unwilling to cooperate. The sample studied is thus not representative of any specific universe, and no generalization of the findings should be made without extensive replication of the study for other samples of middle-aged, middle-class persons. Since our cases are married couples, our direct comparison of men and women is justified. Differences are reported only if they are statistically reliable at the 5 per cent level of confidence. We are also justified in considering the population as middle-class, since 90 per cent of the students described their parents either as "upper-middle" or "lower-middle" class. The questionnaires were anonymous, and they contained a note indicating that the investigator had no interest in identifying respondents as individuals, but there was a conspicuous number on each questionnaire to permit the matching of each wife's questionnaire with that of her husband. Our measure of life satisfaction was provided by the question "In general, how satisfied are you with your life?" with a check-list of five possible answers. The answers to this question were cross-tabulated with a number of others hypothesized to have relationships with life satisfaction, and the figures are reported on the following pages. Since there were so few persons indicating dissatisfaction, the answers "average," "somewhat dissatisfied" and "very dissatisfied" were combined into a rubric arbitrarily called "relatively dissatisfied."

Let us first consider the relation between life satisfaction and certain aspects of the marriage. The data show that the relatively dissatisfied women are more likely than the satisfied women to have married under the age of 20 years (20 per cent compared to 6 per cent). There is a lesser (and not statistically reliable) tendency for dissatisfied women to have married at 30 years of age or later (12 per cent as compared to 7 per cent for the satisfied). Among men there does not seem to be any relationship between age of marriage and life satisfaction. The dissatisfied women are also more likely than the satisfied women to say that they wish they had been a little older or a little younger when they got married (48 per cent compared to only 14 per cent). Among men there is only a very slight tendency for dissatisfied men to say they wish they had been a little older when they got married (15 per cent compared with 9 per cent for the satisfied), and no difference in the proportion saying they wish they had married at a younger age. The conclusion seems to be that age of marriage is a significant variable in the life satisfaction of women but not of men, and that women are aware of it as a factor in their life satisfaction. Among women, there is also a relationship between satisfaction and discrepancy between their own age and husband's age: 35 per cent of the relatively dissatisfied women were the same age as their husband or older, among the satisfied women this was true of 27 per cent, and among the very satisfied women it was true of only 17 per cent.

As might be expected, the intimacy of family relations is related to life satisfaction. When the women declared themselves to be very satisfied, in 48 per cent of the cases the college student offspring described the total family life to be "very close"; among "satisfied" mothers this percentage was only 28 per cent, and among the relatively dissatisfied mothers it was only 20 per cent.[3] The same relationship prevailed when the college student offspring was asked to indicate his fondness for his mother and father. The mother's life satisfaction was just as closely related to her child's fondness for his father as it was to the child's fondness for her. The husband's and wife's life satisfaction is highly correlated: 65 per cent of the men whose wives said they were very satisfied with their lives also said they were satisfied, whereas

---

3. Another indication of this same relationship is the fact that only 10 per cent of the college student offspring of relatively dissatisfied mothers report themselves as completely dependent economically on their parents; the comparable figure is 39 per cent when the mothers report themselves satisfied and 32 per cent when the mothers report themselves as very satisfied.

this was true of only 15 per cent of the men whose wives were relatively dissatisfied. No relationship was found between the life satisfaction of women and any of the following: number of children, number or percentage of children living at home, wish that one had a larger or smaller number of children. There was a slight sex difference in that 40 per cent of the women wish they had had more children, while only 30 per cent of the husbands wish this. The number of hours usually spent in housework is related to life satisfaction insofar as there are significantly more of our cases among relatively dissatisfied women who say they spend 60 or more hours a week in housework than among relatively satisfied women (24 per cent as compared to 9 per cent). At the low end of the scale, however — women who spend fewer than 20 hours a week on housework — there is no significant difference between satisfied and dissatisfied women. This suggests that a belief that one is a "slave to housework" — whether that belief be based in fact or not — is associated with these women's dissatisfaction in life. Women who tend to be relatively dissatisfied have no paid household help while women who consider themselves very satisfied include a large proportion (24 per cent) with one or more paid servants. The dissatisfied women, however, get some household assistance from children or husband in at least as large a proportion as among satisfied women.

The simplest explanation of why life satisfaction and having paid servants are related is suggested by the fact that, for our sample of middle-class women, 85 per cent of those who have paid household help are themselves employed in a paying occupation. In view of this, it is very significant that a larger proportion of the satisfied than of the dissatisfied women are employed outside the home at paid tasks (64 per cent compared to 76 per cent). Employed women seem to be more satisfied, and since it is they who have the servants, the fact of having servants is to be considered as related to life satisfaction in the context of the role of being employed. We do not mean that the reduction of the burden of housework through servants does not in itself increase life satisfaction, but that it must be considered that the great majority of those who hire servants have themselves taken on the role of income earner. (The relatively dissatisfied women who are employed are not working at the higher status professional jobs, but this simply corroborates the well-known finding that there is a close association between job status and job satisfaction.)

The smaller proportion of dissatisfied women in paid work is paralleled by a smaller proportion of them active in some voluntary organization or community activity (48 per cent as compared to 61 per cent among the satisfied). The relationship is in the same direction for men but seems to be stronger (52 per cent compared to 81 per cent). Formal social participation thus either contributes to or reflects life satisfaction. Associated with this finding is a slight relationship between life satisfaction and frequency of going out evenings with the spouse. Among women, 33 per cent of the very satisfied and satisfied women, as compared to 40 per cent of the relatively dissatisfied women, say they go out two or fewer evenings a month with their husbands. Among the men, 29 per cent of the very satisfied, 37 per cent of the satisfied, and 39 per cent of the relatively dissatisfied report going out two or fewer evenings a month with their wives. The relationship is small, but again there seems to be a relationship between social participation and life satisfaction.

Engaging in hobbies cannot be considered a social role, but it is an activity that can substitute, at least partially, for the declining roles of housewife and mother as middle age comes on. The data show a slight relationship between life satisfaction and engaging in hobbies, but since the relationship is true for men as well as for women, this finding does not particularly support our general hypothesis.

Thus far we have examined mainly the relationship of certain objective characteristics of the lives of persons to their life satisfaction. We now turn to a consideration of the relationship of certain *attitudes* held by people to their life satisfaction. The shift of orientation is thus from "what kinds of persons feel generally dissatisfied with their lives?" to "what specific dissatisfactions are most closely associated with the general dissatisfaction that we are here primarily concerned with?" We have already seen how desire for a different age of marriage is associated with general dissatisfaction with life, especially among women. The desire for a later age of marriage often means a desire for longer schooling, and we now see that desire for longer schooling is related to the general sense of dissatisfaction with life. Among women 76 per cent of the relatively dissatisfied believe that further schooling would be desirable whereas this is true of only 61 per cent of the very satisfied; among men the comparable figures are 73 and 55 per cent, respectively. It should not be thought that those who are relatively dissatisfied with their lives in general are inclined to complain about every specific aspect of their lives. There is no association, for example, between general life satisfaction and desire to have had more or fewer children, among either wives or husbands.

The finding that lack of remunerative employment and low job status are factors in women's general dissatisfaction gets further support from another finding that a significantly larger proportion of them believe they should be doing something else by way of occupation: 52 per cent of the relatively dissatisfied women believe they are in the "right job" as compared to 75 per cent of the very satisfied women and 84 per cent of the satisfied women. This desire for a new occupation or role on the part of a significant number of the relatively dissatisfied women is to be contrasted with the lack of difference among our three groups of women in desire to participate in different organizations and community activities (the same is true among men). In so far as lack of participation is a factor in their general dissatisfaction with life, they are unconscious of it, whereas many are conscious of the effect a different occupation might have on their life satisfaction. Among men, the dissatisfaction with occupation is not so great as among women: 79 per cent of the relatively dissatisfied men believe they are in the "right job" as compared to 89 per cent of the very satisfied men and 96 per cent of the satisfied men. This points up the relative lack of preparation of women for change in their central role in middle age, which is part of our major hypothesis.

Desire for having more amusement is associated with life satisfaction among both women and men. A significantly larger proportion of the relatively dissatisfied wives and husband (44 and 39 per cent, respectively) than of the satisfied ones (22 and 13 per cent, respectively) would like to go out more often in the evenings for entertainment than they do now. The same relationship holds when this diversion is specified to take place with the spouse (52 and 64 per cent of the relatively dissatisfied women and men, as compared to 33 and 40 per cent of the very satisfied). There is a slight difference between the sexes, however: women are more likely than men to express a general desire to go out more often evenings, but men are more likely to indicate a desire to go out with their spouses. The data also show that the more satisfied wives and husbands would spend more time in work around the house than the less satisfied ones. There is a sex difference here again, however: a larger proportion of the dissatisfied wives (44 per cent as compared to 27 per cent among the satisfied) want to spend less time in work around the house, whereas this difference is not found among husbands. The total pattern of answers of the dissatisfied women suggests that, for a significant proportion of them, the desire to get a paying occupation and to go out evenings is closely tied up with the desire to spend less time in work around the house.

Conclusion. We have examined the relationships between expressed sense of life satisfaction and various other factors, with a special interest in seeing how these relationships reflect the different central roles of men and women who are of the middle class and are entering middle age. Our major hypothesis, that there are different relationships for men and women, seems to be supported, in part at least, by the specific findings:

1) Women who marry at "too young" or "too old" an age are more likely to be dissatisfied with their lives when their children grow up than are women who marry between the ages of 20 and 30. The data do not show this to be true of men. Age affects the life-satisfaction of middle-aged women in another way: those who are the same age or older than their husband are more likely to be dissatisfied than those who are younger than their hus-

bands. We can speculate that marrying "too young" is a cause of dissatisfaction because it prevents learning the skills which women need to change their central role in middle life. This is supported by the finding that the relatively dissatisfied women are more likely than the satisfied women to believe that further schooling would have been desirable (this relation is also found among men but it seems to have nothing to do with age of marriage). Marrying at "too old" an age, or at an older age than the husband, may cause dissatisfaction among middle-aged women by giving them the feeling that they cannot keep up with their husbands, whose social roles are much the same as in earlier years whereas those of women have inevitably changed.

2) Dissatisfied women are less likely to have assumed a paying job and are more likely to claim that they are spending an inordinate amount of time in housework than are satisfied women. We can speculate that their dissatisfaction arises, in part, from the fact that they are trying to hold onto a social role — that of home-making — which has partly disappeared as their children have grown up. This interpretation is buttressed by the fact that the dissatisfied women, who spend most time around the house, are least likely to have a close family life and most likely to have their college student children already partly financially independent. The interpretation is also supported by the fact that dissatisfied women are more likely to feel they should be engaged in some occupation other than the one they now have. A seemingly contrary fact is that the satisfied women are more likely to have hired servants to help with the housework, but this may simply indicate that women with paying occupations are the ones who hire servants to do the heavy tasks around the house.

3) Social participation is associated with life satisfaction among both men and women. We measured social participation both in terms of hours per week spent in organizations and community activities and in terms of number of evenings out with spouse. Social participation seems to be a direct cause of life satisfaction, since the two are associated for both sexes, but social participation may also operate indirectly for women since

it is a role different from home-making and a paying occupation and can thus be an additional role when homemaking declines. This latter possibility gains support by the finding that the dissatisfied women would like to spend less time in work around the house, whereas this is not true for dissatisfied men.

While this study must be extensively replicated before its finding can be generalized, it does point to a verification of our major hypothesis that the life satisfaction of middle-class women as they enter middle age is a function of the degree to which they are able to assume another central role to substitute for their necessarily declining role as homemakers. The data indicate that earning an income and engaging in organizational activities are among the additional roles that make for life satisfaction, but the study makes no pretense of specifying all of them or of indicating what the background of successful assumption of a new role may be.

EMPLOYMENT PROBLEMS OF
OLDER WORKERS*

ARTHUR M. and JANE N. ROSS

INTRODUCTION

MEN and women begin to encounter special problems of
employment opportunity as they pass from youth into middle age. These problems intensify as the years go by; additional
problems are met as retirement age is reached. It should not be
thought, however, that older workers make up a homogeneous
group. There is a basic distinction between those who have regular jobs and those who have been thrown on the labor market.
Even among the latter group there are great differences. A woman of 50 having excellent stenographic skills, residing in a fast-
growing area, and enjoying good health will have little or
no difficulty finding employment. Another woman of the same
age who has been laid off from a textile factory, the only major
firm in her community, and who has no other marketable skill,
will experience difficulty.

A report of the New York State joint Legislative Committee of
Problems of the Aging makes the point in these words:

> The inclusion of all persons aged 45 years and over into
> a classification labeled "older jobseekers" suggests that there is
> a single group of so-called older workers in the labor force.
> * * * A floor girl is "old" at 40, a 65-year-old patternmaker
> is respected, accepted, and often preferred to a younger work-
> er * * * So much depends on the kind and degree of skill
> involved, the industry, labor market, degree of unionization,
> and the personal qualities of the individual worker, that a
> single grouping of workers over 45 as older workers is a fiction,
> not a fact.

---

* *Studies In Unemployment.* Prepared for the Special Committee on Unemployment Problems, United States Senate, 86th Congress, 2nd Session,
pp. 97-101.

Likewise facile generalizations concerning persons of retirement age should be avoided. As Prof. Wilbur Cohen has said:

> It is extremely misleading and erroneous as a matter of public policy to think of 15 million people as having all of the same characteristics, all of the same problems, all of the same needs.

For some purposes, however, it is necessary to have arbitrary dividing lines. The conventional ages of 45 and 65 are frequently used to designate the onset of middle age and of old age. Much is said about the aging of the population and the labor force. If an increasing percentage of older persons is meant, the maturing process has largely been completed. The percentage of the population 45 and over will be the same in 1975 (28.8 per cent, as estimated by the Census Bureau) as it was in 1955. The proportion 65 and over will increase from 8.9 to 9.3 per cent. In the same period the proportion of persons 45 and over in the labor force will rise slightly from 36.1 to 36.7 per cent, while the group 65 and over will fall from 4.8 to 4.4 per cent.

Percentages aside, the numbers involved have been increasing rapidly and will continue to do so. The number of persons 45 and over in the total population increased from 13.5 million in 1900 to 47.6 million in 1955. By 1975, it is estimated, there will be 63.8 million in this category. For persons 65 and over the corresponding figures are 3.1 million in 1900, 14.1 million in 1955, and 20.7 million in 1975. In the labor force, there were 6.7 million over 45 in 1900 and 24.9 in 1955; the estimate for 1975 is 33.5 million. There were 1.1 million 65 and over in the labor force in 1900, 3.3. million in 1955, and there will be an estimated 4.1 million in 1975.

DEVELOPMENTS AFFECTING OLDER WORKERS' EMPLOYMENT PROSPECTS

Apart from these population trends, other long-run economic and social changes have accentuated the employment problems of older workers.

1) Decline in Self-employment. Opportunities for self-employment where artificial age barriers are not significant, have diminished. We are now a Nation of wage and salary earners; more than 80 per cent of gainfully employed Americans are in the hire of others. Consolidation of farm ownership has been particularly important in reducing the opportunities for older men. The number of farms in the United States, which stood at 6,448,000 in 1920, had fallen to 4,783,000 by 1954.

2) Dominance of Large Firms. It is well known that large firms have become dominant in many industries. As we shall indicate below, the large firm is more likely to have a maximum hiring age. As a result of systematic seniority and promotion-from-within policies, the mature worker on the inside has more protection; but since hiring is largely restricted to low-paid entry jobs, the mature worker on the outside has less opportunity even in the absence of discrimination. In large employing units the adjustment of work duties to diminishing physical strength and the development of part-time work schedules become more difficult, particularly under collective bargaining. Hence an abrupt transition from full-time regular employment to complete retirement is likely.

3) Changes in Family Structure have accentuated the problem of income maintenance in later middle age and in old age. Separate households are now the rule even for retired individual and couples. The economic difficulties of the older generation are not so easily absorbed in the total earning capacity of the "extended" family as they formerly were.

> The immense mobility of our society, and perpetually changing personality of each neighborhood, the diminishing communications between separated generation * * * have driven wedges of social distance between the various family levels.

4) Shifts in Occupational Structure. The pace of economic change has been increasing steadily and has accelerated particularly since the end of World War II. Occupational structure, industry mix, and the location of economic activity have all been affected.

We have already noted the decline in the number of farmers and other self-employed persons in the labor force. Certain other changes might have been expected to operate in favor of the older worker, but employer hiring preferences have worked in the other direction. Brawn and muscle are less frequently the primary factors in job performance. The proportion of unskilled workers in the work force fell continuously from 36 per cent in 1910 to 19.3 per cent in 1950, and is even lower at the present time. At the same time the proportion of professional persons has advanced from 4.4 to 7.3 per cent. It is generally believed that job performance holds up better with advancing age in professional endeavors than in most other lines of work. Similarly, the proportion of nonagricultural proprietors, managers, and officials has risen from 6.5 to 8.7 per cent in the same period, seemingly increasing the need for the experience and judgment of older persons. In addition the great expansion of clerical, sales, and other white-collar employment has provided potential outlets for the middle-aged women who have been reentering the labor market to an increasing extent once they have passed beyond the child-bearing period. The proportion of clerks and kindred workers in the labor force rose from 10.2 per cent in 1910 to 21 per cent in 1950, and is probably higher today.

Studies of employer hiring policies uniformly show, however, that upper age limitations are specified most frequently in clerical, sales, professional, and managerial openings (together with unskilled labor). These are also the occupational groups with the most restrictive age limits.

For example, the Department of Labor reports that in a recent survey, 35 per cent of clerical job openings specified upper age limits of under 35, 57 per cent under 45, and 67 per cent under 55. Thus the changes in occupational structure have been a mixed blessing at best.

5) Educational Obsolescence. If upper age limits could be relaxed, the occupational distribution of the 1960's might well be more receptive to older wage and salary earners than that which existed half a century ago. But even in that event, educational obsolescence would make the transition a difficult one. Educational obsolescence is an important cause of the employment difficulties of older workers. Eliminating educational deficiencies must be an important part of any program to improve their employment opportunities. So long as our economy remains dynamic, however, it is likely that the problem will remain.

> Obsolescence of skills is part of the price of social progress. At any given time the aged population will reflect the patterns of education, of training and of developed skills acquired a generation or more before. So far the economy has progressed and has therefore developed or demanded new skills, so far as it likely that the aged will be less well equipped than the young to cope with the new requirements. Although attention should be given to mitigating this obsolescence, it seems at least strongly probable that it could never be overcome.

Educational obsolescence has several facets. First, of course, is the extension of customary or compulsory years of schooling. The extent of the change was dramatically pointed up by a recent Government survey of older jobseekers in seven major labor market areas. Among the applicants between 45 and 64 years of age, scarcely two out of three had completed elementary school. Second, established skills often become unmarketable. Declining blue-collar employment and increasing white-collar employment accentuate the problem. In the study just cited, it was found that: *a*) more than two out of five jobseekers had held their previous job in manufacturing; *b*) only about one-quarter came from white-collar occupations; *c*) those with white-collar skills were reemployed much more rapidly. This experience seems to be typical. Third, many new jobs have developed which simply did not exist a generation ago. Electronics technician provides a case in point. Finally, there are changes in the content of existing jobs. We are told, for example, that older auto mechanics are unemployed in some cases not because of any slack in the trade but because they lack experience and training in automatic transmissions.

6) Declining and Expanding Industries. In a period of rapid economic change some industries are growing while others shrink. New industries tend to staff themselves with young workers. On the other hand, there is a large proportion of older workers in the declining industries because new employees are not being hired and because only those employees with high seniority can retain jobs. In 1953, for example, 53 per cent of male employees in the anthracite coal industry were 45 years and over, as compared with 27.7 per cent in the crude petroleum and natural gas industry; 42 per cent in apparel manufacturing, as compared with 26.2 per cent in electrical manufacturing; 42.5 per cent in local transit lines, as compared with 25.2 per cent in trucking and warehousing and 13.2 per cent in air transportation. Thus there is some tendency to segregate older workers in the declining industries where they are cut off from the opportunities associated with industrial growth.

7) Industrial Migration. Geographical movement of industry has a serious impact on the employment of older workers. Two types of movement are of importance here. The first is relocation from the center of a city out to the suburban portions of the labor market. Suburban housing is largely occupied by younger families. Older couples and individuals, along with minority racial and national groups, are left in the central areas, increasingly isolated from the more modern and rapidly growing industrial establishments. Second is interregional migration of industry, notably the movement of textile firms from New England to the south. Between 1947 and 1954 textile employment fell more than 26 per cent in the New England States, while increasing in the South Atlantic and East South Central States. Many studies have been made of the subsequent experience of workers laid off because of plant shutdowns and migrations. These studies uniformly show that older workers have more difficulty than younger workers in becoming readjusted. W. H. Miernyk recently surveyed displaced textile workers in a number of Massachusetts communities. He found that 45 per cent had been reemployed by the time of the survey. This was true, however, of only 42 per cent of those between 46 and 55, 28 per cent of those between 56 and 65, and 2 per cent of those over 64.

8) Spread of Formal Pension and Retirement Systems. Although industrial pension plans were introduced as early as the 19th century, they have only become widespread during the past decade. These plans affect the employment problems of older

workers in at least three ways. 1) Together with old-age and survivors insurance and equivalent public programs, they provide
a financial solution for the worker of retirement age who can no
longer obtain employment, or is no longer able to work, or no
longer wishes to work. 2) They frequently include compulsory
retirement provisions under which the worker may be required
to relinquish his job upon reaching retirement age, even though
he might prefer to continue at work. 3) Pension plans accentuate
employer preference for hiring younger workers. The recent
survey of older worker adjustment in seven labor market areas
established that workers over 45 constituted 33 per cent of the
labor force in firms with pension plans, as compared with 35
per cent in firms without plans. More significantly, among the
new hires in firms with pension plans, only 15 per cent were
45 and over. In contrast, these older workers constituted 25 per
cent of new hires in the firms without pension plans.

JOB COUNSELING AND PLACEMENT
SERVICES FOR PERSONS OVER 40*

CHARLES E. ODELL

DESPITE the recent recession, forecasts of the United States
Labor Department of Labor indicate that job prospects for
middle-aged and older workers should improve in the next few
years. In a publication entitled *Our Manpower Future,*[1] the
Department projects a further dramatic increase in gross national
products in the next few years which will require a corresponding increase of about 10 million workers in the labor force. Since
there will continue to be a comparative shortage of workers in
the age group from 25 to 44, the Department indicates that at
least half of the 10 million additional workers will have to be
drawn from the group of men and women over 45. The recently
published Rockefeller Brothers Report[2] also bears out the optimism of the Department of Labor's earlier findings.

Whether this forecast becomes a reality depends upon a number of factors. Three of the most important of these factors will
be: 1) our will and determination to regain and sustain a full
employment economy 2) the extent to which employer prej-
udices against workers over 40 can be overcome, and 3) the
extent and effectiveness of job counseling and placement services
to help older job seekers find new employment. The central purpose of this article is to describe briefly the various types of
programs that have been developed to help these workers find
new jobs.

PUBLICLY SUPPORTED SERVICES

The most universally available counseling and placement services for workers over 40 are provided through the facilities of the

* *Geriatrics 14:* 518-522 August 1959.

1,800 local offices of the state employment services affiliated with
the United States Employment Service of the United States Department of Labor. In the past ten years, through a series of
intensive studies and research projects, the number and quality
of employment service personnel available to serve the job seeker
over 40 has been greatly increased. In July 1956, the Secretary
of Labor authorized each state to establish and maintain specialized counseling and placement services for older workers,
and, since that time, virtually every state has set up such facilities in most major city employment offices. The United States
Employment Service has developed and published a handbook
and training guide for older workers specialists, and an estimated 1,500 people have been trained to provide special services
for these workers.[3-4] Several states, such as New York, have also
passed bills establishing special services and appropriating state
funds, in addition to the customary federal grants, to finance
them.

Specifically, what special services are provided to the over-
40 age group by the public employment offices? Among the services provided without any fee or charge to worker or employer
are:

Intensive review of qualifications to discover new skills and to
refurbish old ones;

Careful appraisal of interests and aptitudes, using scientifically
standardized psychologic tests when appropriate;

Evaluation of physical capacities and abilities with the help
of the family physician or a specialist in industrial medical
practice;

Informing the applicant about current job requirements and
opportunities;

Counseling, to assist the worker in choosing new fields of
work or in training or retraining to broaden or refurbish skills
in old fields;

Group consultation with workers having common problems in
job seeking to help them plan and conduct a job search; and

Selective placement, whenever there is evidence of physical
disability or slowing down, to protect the worker and the employer from health and safety hazards.

SELF-HELP SERVICES

A unique self-help type of service available to the middle-aged and older job seeker is provided by the Forty Plus Clubs, which exist in a dozen or more major cities throughout the United States. These services are limited to men over 40 who have lost their jobs in the professional, managerial, technical, or selling fields or who have earned a minimum of perhaps $5,000 or more per year. Usually a small membership fee is charged in order to finance the club's office space and services, but the effort is primarily one of self-help through having the active (unemployed) members contact employers to develop job openings which other active members can fill. Until the economic downturn of 1957-58, these clubs were reporting some success as evidenced by the fact that most of them were actively recruiting members to fill job openings which were available. Since that time, the number of such workers looking for jobs has increased, so that most of the clubs now seem to have a surplus of unemployed members and a shortage of suitable jobs to offer them.

PRIVATELY FINANCED, NONPROFIT ORGANIZATIONS

There are a number of organizations throughout the country which provide special counseling and placement services for the worker over 40 which are financed by United Fund Drives or other sources of private funds. The most widespread of these are the Jewish Vocational Services, which exist in many large cities, the YMCA-YWCA Placement Services, and the Catholic Archdiocesan Employment Services.

In a few cities, other privately financed organizations have provided successful job-finding services, including Careers Unlimited for Mature Women of San Francisco; the Cleveland Vocational Guidance Bureau, an affiliate of the Cleveland Welfare Federation; the Over 40 Club of Charlotte, North Carolina; Senior Consultants, Inc., of Nassau County, New York; and Over 60 Club of Arlington, Virginia.

PRIVATE, FEE-CHARGING AGENCIES

In a survey conducted several years ago, Albert J. Abrams, executive director of the New York State Joint Legislative Committee on Problems of the Aging, reported on the attitudes and practices of private, fee-charging employment agencies toward older workers.[5] The attitude of such agencies toward the middle-aged and older worker at that time was not very encouraging because they seemed to feel, generally, that it was their job to satisfy the employer's hiring specifications rather than to sell the qualifications of their older clients. More recently, there seems to be a growing interest in the older worker in private agencies, particularly if they are qualified in those fields of work in which there is a shortage of manpower, such as science; engineering; certain skilled trades; and certain clerical, sales, and service occupations. For example, there is the service of Manpower, Inc., of Milwaukee and 80 other cities, which provides a contractual service to employers with special manpower problems requiring part-time or "special duties" personnel to perform special projects such as taking inventories or filling seasonal rush orders. Manpower, Inc., actively recruits middle-aged and older workers, particularly women who want work on a part-time basis.

VOLUNTARY EFFORTS BY WOMEN'S ORGANIZATIONS

Under the stimulation of the Women's Bureau of the Department of Labor, which has held Earning Opportunities Forums for Mature Women[6] in a number of communities, some of the national and international women's organizations, such as Altrusa, Zonta, Soroptimists, American Association of University Women, and the Business and Professional Women's Clubs, are conducting local, statewide, and even "national" programs to increase job opportunities for mature women and to improve their work habits and skills. Altrusa and Zonta have been primarily interested in stimulating employment opportunities for middle-aged and older office and sales workers, AAUW has been most interested in encouraging more "mature" women with college training to enter or reenter the teaching profession, BPW has worked most extensively in conducting small business clinics for mature women, and the Soroptimists have cooperated with other community groups to provide placement and counseling services.

SHELTERED AND PART-TIME EMPLOYMENT

Although sheltered workshops are customarily associated with the physically handicapped, there is increasing interest in the development of such programs for the older worker who is retired and needs part-time employment to supplement his income. Goodwill Industries have conducted such programs for significant numbers of older workers for many years. More recently, the Jewish Vocational Services in a number of cities have developed workshops for older workers with the assistance of special grants from the Federal Office of Vocational Rehabilitation in order to increase the work tolerance of older workers and to prepare as many as possible for reentry in competitive employment. A unique experiment of this type is being conducted in Chicago by Senior Achievement, Inc., with the support of several major employers who subcontract the production of small parts and special articles to the workshops. Another such enterprise is AGE, Inc., of St. Paul, Minnesota, set up by a private physician to help some of his older patients supplement their retirement incomes or to find new jobs.

INFORMATION AND REFERRAL SERVICES

A growing number of communities have established information and referral services for older and retired workers which are helpful in suggesting agencies and employers who can be of assistance in helping older persons get and hold jobs. Usually such services are not confined to employment information but will include it as part of an over-all service. An outstanding example is the Los Angeles County Senior Citizens Service Center financed by the County Board of Supervisors. In other communities, such service is provided by the Community Chest or United Community Services Organization through a central unit or a special council on aging and the aged. Some states, such as Massachusetts, have organized community councils on aging on a statewide basis to provide such service, while others, such as Pennsylvania, have statewide councils with subcommittees on employment. For more information about such services, those interested in jobs for workers over 40 should contact one of the following organizations:

The local office of State Employment Service serving the community;

The local Council on Aging or Senior Citizens Service Center, if one exists;

The State Council on Aging; or

The Federal Council on Aging, which is located in the Department of Health, Education, and Welfare in Washington, D.C.

CONCLUSIONS

While some of the activities and services reported here are comparatively limited in scope and may be confined to one or a few communities, it seems clear that there is increasing interest in the employment needs and problems of the worker over 40. With this very evident increase in the interest and support of public and private groups, it seems safe to predict that counseling and job finding services for older workers will continue to grow and that the need for qualified, older workers forecast by the Department of Labor for the next eight years will be met, if, as, and when it materializes.

The recent recession has, however, greatly increased the number of middle-aged and older unemployed workers. While some of these will be recalled on the basis of seniority provisions in labor contracts, there is some evidence to indicate that we may be developing a "pocket" of hard core unemployment among displaced older workers. While existing placement and counseling services may help some of these older workers, it would seem that additional services are also needed in the fields of vocational retraining, adult education, and vocational rehabilitation. The reason for this is fairly obvious—the jobs formerly performed by these older workers have either been radically changed by advancing technology or they no longer exist. There is, therefore, no room for complacency in the short run, despite the optimism of long-range forecasts.

Physicians working with middle-aged and older persons in private and industrial medical practice can make a significant contribution to the employment and employability of their patients by getting acquainted with those agencies in the community that have been set up to assist the older worker in finding new employment. The specialist in internal medicine or geriatrics may have general knowledge of jobs and job requirements, but frequently this is not the case. Similarly, the public and private agencies may have general knowledge of technics used in the appraisal of physical capacity and its relationship to jobs and job requirements, but they would certainly benefit from closer worker relationships with the medical profession in getting competent medical opinions on the work capacities and tolerances of job applicants. By working more closely together, doctors and vocational experts can do much to overcome road blocks to new employment for middle-aged and older workers who are also physically disabled or in some way slowed down by normal aging or the onset of one or more of the so-called "chronic diseases."

REFERENCES

1. *Our Manpower Future, 1955-65.* Washington, D.C. U.S. Department of Labor, Superintendent of Documents, 1956.
2. *The Challenge to America: Its Economic and Social Aspects.* Report of Panel of Special Studies Project, America at Midcentury Series. Rockefeller Brothers Fund, New York, Doubleday Inc., 1958.
3. *Services to Older Workers by the Public Employment Service.* BES. No. E-169, Washington, D.C., U.S. Department of Labor, Bureau of Employment Security, 1957.
4. *Services to Older Workers.* Employment Office Training Program, Unit 16 Parts A and B and chart book. Washington, D.C., Bureau of Employment Security, 1957
5. Abrams, A. J.: Private employment agencies and the older worker, in *Enriching the Years.* Report of the New York State Joint Legislative Committee on Problems of the Aging, Legislative Department #32, Albany, New York, 1953.
6. *How to Conduct an Earning Opportunities Forum.* Washington, D.C., U.S. Department of Labor, Women's Bureau, Leaflet 25, Superintendent of Documents, 1956.

FAMILY TENSIONS BETWEEN THE OLD AND THE MIDDLE-AGED[*]

RUTH SHONLE CAVAN, Ph.D.

OVER the past thirty years special needs of old people have gradually been recognized and met. Financial needs, better health care, suitable recreation, adequate housing, and retirement jobs have all been at least partially provided.

Primary Group Needs. Perhaps the most fundamental need of old people, however, is for the intimate and affectionate contacts in a primary group. This need is either not recognized or is passed over lightly in discussions of old age.

At every age level except old age, the need for intimate contacts is recognized—in fact, stressed. The significance of marriage is said to lie in its close companionship; the child's need for loving care by the parents has never been more strongly emphasized. But suddenly, in old age, men and women long accustomed to primary group life are assumed no longer to need it.

Actually, old people are in great need of belonging to some intimate group. Many old people have lost the mate who supplied affection. Approximately one third of all men and two thirds of all women aged sixty-five and over are without wife or husband, the great majority being widowers or widows.[1] The decades add years and deaths, until among the small number who remain at age eighty-five and over, about 60 per cent of the men and 85 per cent of the women are widowed.[2] These stranded old people are the olds who speak of loneliness, of no

[*] *Marriage and Family Living*, November 1956, pp. 323-327.

1. *Statistical Abstract of the United States, 1954.* Washington Government Printing Office, 1954, p. 263.
2. Ruth Shonle Cavan: *The American Family.* Thomas Y. Crowell Co., 1953, p. 590.

one caring, of neglect by children, and of the uselessness of living.

In addition to these solitary individuals are old couples. The need for love is not so apparent as long as an old couple is able to remain physically self-sufficient. But the old couple in ill health or with failing strength feels much the same need that a child feels for the sympathetic and protective care of someone who is attached to him by affection and loyalty.

The family is the group in our society designated to supply love. The living arrangements of old people give some indication of the accessibility of the family as a source of affection. Among men aged seventy-five and over, out of every hundred, forty-one live with the wife, thirty-four live with other relatives, chiefly children, in either their own or the relatives' home, and twenty-five live alone or in institutions, hotels, lodging houses, and the like.[3] Of every hundred women aged seventy-five and over, seventeen live with the husband and fifty-one with other relatives, primarily children; thirty-two live alone, in institutions, hotels, and the like.

Mutual Rejection. When old people live with children or other relatives, the relationships are not always happy, nor are they always cordial between adult children and old parents who live separately from each other. Respectable middle-aged people have been heard to make such remarks as these about their parents: "You ought to take every person over sixty-five out and shoot him," or, rhetorically, "Why don't the old fools die," or more generally, "What we need is more homes for the old." Social workers whose clientele includes old people sometimes share this rejecting attitude. In one published article, perhaps somewhat extreme, a social worker speaks of people "sacrificing" their lives for their parents and becoming "bitter, frustrated, warped" individuals.[4] The same article concedes that the child owes his parents a definite responsibility but not so "overwhelming that it stifles his own life" or "jeopardizes

---

3. Based on *United States Census of Population, Special Report PE No. 2D.* Washington, Government Printing Office, 1953, pp. 21-22.
4. Margaret B. Ryder: "Case Work with the Aged Parent and His Adult Children. *The Family,* 26: 243-50, November, 1945.

his own family relationships"—meaning relationships to spouse
and children, but excluding parents from the concept of the
family.

At the same time that middle-aged children reject their parents, they also feel a sense of duty toward them and of guilt if
they are not cared for or if they are placed in an institution instead of being cared for in the family.

Old people also vary in their feelings. They want independence
and resent interference from their children. At the same time
they complain of neglect and yearn for the love and affection of
their children.

Social Change and Conflict. Some writers have assumed that
conflict between old and middle-aged is inevitable. It seems,
however, that much of the conflict is due to contemporary social
changes and types of family organization resulting from these
changes. If it is true that conflict grows out of temporary social
changes, then, as these situations become stabilized or pass into
social history, it seems probable that the present strained relations between old parents and middle-aged children may also
change. This paper will examine some of the probable social
causes for the conflict between old and middle-aged; personality
conflicts per se are not included in the discussion.

The basis of many seeming personality conflicts is, in reality,
some form of cultural conflict, of which there are three types,
all based on cultural transition. These three types of transition
are from rural to urban, from foreign culture to American, and
fom lower to higher class status. Each of these transitions is
typically made by one small family unit, usually the younger
generation moving to the new position, while the parent generation remains in the original cultural position.

1) *Rural to urban transition.* Young people who move from
farm to city readily adapt themselves to urban values and modes
of behavior. Present-day middle-aged people who were born
and reared on farms usually are thoroughly urbanized. Their
parents who remained on their farms tend to be rural in outlook on life, chiefly because their attitudes were firmly set before
present means of mass communication and easy transportation

had developed. The clash of rural-urban values between the two generations was clearly demonstrated by Dinkel in his study of fifty Minnesota families, reported in 1943.[5] The conflict was increased by the authoritarianism of the old parents who felt that their position entitled them to insist upon compliance with their values, whereas their children felt entitled to follow their own more urbanized values.

2) *Foreign to American culture.* The great influx of foreign-born people between 1890 and 1914 is now part of the social history of the United States. The young foreigners who came then are old people now. For example, in one small industrial city which drew many immigrants, when 16 per cent of the total population was foreign-born, 45 per cent of persons aged sixty-five and over were foreign-born.[6]

The old age group among the foreign-born is often still loyal to many of the precepts and customs of the foreign culture, whereas their middle-aged children have pulled away from their parents and tend to identify themselves with their more Americanized children. Tensions between old parents and their children tend to originate in cultural conflicts. An interesting experiment in family-life education for a group of aged Jews in St. Louis revealed that the subject of most interest was the old people's feeling of rejection by their children.[7] The leaders of the group concluded that in addition to the usual adjustments of the old, this group had also to adjust to the cultural alienation from their Americanized children with its attendant feeling of isolation and rejection.

3) *Upward social mobility.* In the United States upward mobility is taken for granted. Sons enter occupations requiring more education and commanding higher salaries than the occupations of their fathers; for their sons they plan still more educa-

---

5. Robert M. Dinkel: Parent-Child Conflict in Minnesota Families, *American Sociological Review*, 8: 412-19, 1943.
6. Ruth Shonle Cavan: Old Age in a City of 100,000. *Illinois Academy of Science Transactions*, 40: 156-70, 1947. Figures are for 1940 and not available for later dates.
7. Sidney Hurwitz and Jacob C. Guthartz: Family Life Education with the Aged. *Social Casework*, 33: 382-87, 1952.

tion and a further push upward. In the upward climb, it is not sufficient that the climber should affiliate himself with the class level above him, assimilating their culture; he must also break his identification with the class level left behind, most often represented by his parents. In an exploratory study, LeMasters tested the hypothesis that social class differences are a factor in creating tension between old people and their upwardly mobile children. His cases tended to show that rural-urban differences and differences in educational and social class level were all related to difficulties in joint living of parents and their married children. When these differences were not present, "parents seemed to live quite harmoniously with their married children, barring such personal factors as personality problems" (not covered by the study).[8]

Upward social mobility often is closely related to one of the other two types of cultural transition — rural to urban or foreign to American culture. The chasm between old parents and middle-aged children is wider and deeper when two, rather than one, types of cultural transition are involved.

The Effect of Small Family Units. Adjustment to the cultural conflicts just discussed and to the geographic mobility accompanying cultural change has included the breaking of the family into generational units, with each unit consisting of the parent generation and their dependent children. As the children mature, they in turn establish independent households and detach themselves from their parents. When we say "family," we customarily refer to husband, wife, and dependent children; rarely do we include grandparents in the concept of the family. This limited concept of the family has many implications.

1) Each small family unit becomes autonomous. It not only lives in its own domicile but jealously guards its privacy and its right to determine its own family pattern of living. The autonomy of the generations is established when the younger couple are about twenty-five years of age and the parental couple about fifty. The question of joint living — or even close interdependence — does not arise until some twenty-five years later when the

8. L. L. LeMasters: Unpublished study; quotation from personal letter.

couples are respectively fifty and seventy-five years old. In the
meantime a quarter of a century of separate living has caused
the two couples to become firmly set in their disparate ways of
family life.

2) Separate family units call for complementary roles within
each unit, which become competitive roles between the units.
Each daughter becomes a homemaker and each son an independent head of his family. Thus daughter and mother have
identical and hence competitive roles; son and father likewise
have identical and competitive roles. These roles are necessary
as long as the two families remain separate. If in the old age
of the parents, the two households merge or even increase their
inter-family contacts, the roles compete. Mother and daughter
compete, and father and son. Sometimes instead of peaceful
competition, there is conflict.

3) Small family units conceal latent conflict over authority.
The older authoritarian type of family life, fitted to a culturally
stable rural society, has given way to a more equalitarian type
of family life. The present middle-aged generation is the critical
generation in the transition from authoritarian to the equalitarian family where old and young alike have a voice in decision-
making. The present old generation is the last of the truly authoritarian generations of parents. The present middle-aged generation waged the battle for freedom in the 1920's and out-
wardly at least won the battle. The interaction between old and
middle-aged, observed in many cases and indirectly revealed in
many studies, raises the question whether the parents really
changed their authoritarian attitudes; and whether the children
really achieved equality and independence. Perhaps the old
attitudes remain but have been kept in abeyance by the geographical separation of households. When the old age of the
parents brings them into closer contact with their middle-aged
children, the old struggle often seems to revive. The middle-age
alternately submit and rebel, sometimes bursting into tears or
temper tantrums in true adolescent fashion. The old, for their
part, try to dominate and bend their sons and daughters to their
will. At the same time, the adult children feel protective toward

their parents, and the parents want affection and sympathy. Thus the chances are great that both old and middle-aged will act with inconsistent behavior because of the inconsistencies within themselves and the struggle between the generations.

Decline of Conflict Situations. The preceding discussion tends to show that the alienation of children from parents is transitional in nature, the concomitant of temporary social changes. Some at least of the changes are already disappearing. The passage from rural to urban will undoubtedly continue as long as the rural birth rate exceeds needs for rural labor, and as long as urban industries expand. However, the cultural rift in this movement is now being nullified by the urbanization of rural life. Ethnic conflicts may remain acute for foreign-born groups, but because of reduction in immigration they will affect a much smaller proportion of the population. Upward social mobility will be made less painful with the decline in the other two types of culture conflict, and with the continued spread of education into the lower class levels. There will continue, however, to be some cultural differences between the generations, due to the speed of cultural change now typical of the United States, which shows no signs of abatement. Only a static society could eliminate all cultural differences between generations.

The conflict between authoritarian oldsters and their middle-aged children may also be expected to decrease. Part of this authoritarianism was fostered by rural and foreign backgrounds. As ruralism and foreign culture disappear, authoritarianism may be expected to decline in favor of a more equalitarian type of family living. Also, the middle-aged people who struggled to break the bonds are less authoritarian with their children, and this hard struggle between the generations may perhaps never be repeated with future generations.

As long as the family breaks off into generational units, the competition of roles will continue if the units try to reunite. Separate dwelling units over a quarter of a century will also continue to lead to the formation of distinctive patterns of family living. However, with reduction in cultural change, the differences in family patterns should be less sharp.

Is Separation the Best Solution? The chief solution offered at present for generational conflicts is separate living quarters, with the institutional nursing home supplanting the independent dwelling as old age decline advances. Old people are urged not to identify themselves closely with their children but to seek friends of their own age. These suggestions are directed at reduction of conflict on a superficial basis by keeping the antagonists apart. They overlook the need of the old for affection and primary group contacts; and they do not explore the benefits that might accrue to old and young alike from closer contacts maintained over the years.

By excluding the old from their lives, younger people feel that they gain freedom to develop their own lives. Do they also lose something by cutting themselves off from the old?

1) *Benefits to adult children.* At the present time, young married people often may profit by close relationships with their parents. One need only mention their need for sharing parental homes during the post war period; the many college-student marriages in need of some family assistance; the dependence of the military-service wife on her parents while her husband is overseas; and the tendency of divorced men and women — perhaps with a child or two — to return to the homes of their respective parents temporarily or permanently. If these early joint family relationships can be amicably arranged, not only does the younger person benefit from the supportive aid of parents, but the basis may be laid for future mutual affection and help whenever either the old or the young branch of the family needs help.[9]

2) *Benefits to granchildren.* Nothing has been said so far about the adjustment between old people and their grandchildren. Once an honored position, the status of grandparent has tended to fall into disrepute. Grandparents are accused of spoiling their grandchildren or, conversely, of being too strict and critical. Other writers concede that there is much of value in

---

9. With a somewhat different approach, Ruth Albrecht discusses the possibilities for constructive intergenerational contacts in Intergenerational Parent Patterns. *Journal of Home Economics,* 46: 29-32, 1954.

the relationship when it is based on love and when the grandparent does not compete with the child's parents.[10]

The longer length of life is increasing materially the proportion of families which have living grandparents. They constitute an untapped source of useful and valuable help, at present not put to use because of the general rejection of the old. Grandparents are often called upon in emergencies, but there are many ways in which grandparents can make a continuing contribution. When affection and protective care of children are as much emphasized as at present, grandparents may provide additional security to children. The inclusion of grandparents in the circle of loving and beloved adults may also prevent too exclusive a relationship from developing between parents and children. Grandparents can also give children a sense of the continuity and unity of family life and some knowledge of their own family history. Mobility has tended to destroy historical contacts and knowledge. Grandparents carry with them in memory and sometimes in documents the past history of the family, which they have received from their parents and grandparents. The memory of a grandparent may span 150 years of family history.

Conclusion. This paper has tried to show that there are specific, identifiable causes for present tensions between old parents and their middle-aged children; that these causes are to some degree temporary in nature; and that they are decreasing in force. In the meantime, attitudes of rejection are becoming fixed and are supported by such rationalizations as the supposition that in-laws cannot live peaceably together, that the middle generation owes sole attention to the oncoming generation, and that old people are better off in institutions than in close association with their children. Separation into small family units and

10. G. A. Strauss: Grandmother Made Johnny Delinquent, *American Journal of Orthopsychiatry,* 13: 343-47, 1943; B. Borden: The Role of the Grandparents in Children's Behavior Problems, *Smith College Studies in Social Work,* 17: 115-16, 1946; Harman Vollmer, The Grandmother: A Problem in Child-rearing. *American Journal of Orthopsychiatry,* 7: 378-83, 1937; Helene Deutsch: *Psychology of Women, A Psychoanalytic Interpretation,* vol. 2, *Motherhood.* New York, Grune, 1945.

mutual rejection are becoming crystallized into a permanent pattern. Such fixation will hinder family adjustment to less conflicting cultural patterns of the future and will reduce the number of mutual benefits that closer family contacts can bring.

INTERGENERATIONAL FAMILY RELATIONSHIPS AND SOCIAL ROLE CHANGES IN MIDDLE AGE*‡

MARVIN B. SUSSMAN, Ph.D.

SOCIAL roles and family relationships in middle age have been studied by a number of investigators (Deutscher, 1959; Gravatt, 1953; Havighurst, 1957; Neugarten and Gutmann, 1958; Sussman, 1953, 1954, 1955, 1956, 1959). Deutscher found that middle-aged parents tend to define the post-parental situation favorably, particularly those who are involved in many other roles beside that of being a parent. The transition from the child-bearing to the postparental stage of the life cycle was not perceived as a crisis by the middle-class members of his sample. Havighurst has developed a rating technique for measuring the quality of performance in each of nine social roles. He found no marked decrease in role performance with age in the years from 40 to 70. The higher more than the lower social classes meet role expectations successfully during this post-parental period. Havighurst also points out that social roles can be ordered by the degree of internalization of role expectations. A relatively high degree of internalization of expectations are found in the first-order roles of worker, parent, spouse, and home-maker. The second-order roles are friend and user of leisure time; and the third-order are citizen, church member, and club and association member. The Havighurst data suggest that changes in behavior in all social roles do not occur simultaneously.

* This research was facilitated by Public Health Service Grant M 1592 and by a grant-in-aid for research from the Social Science Research Council.
   Acknowledgement is made to Mrs. Eleanor Caplan, Research Associate, Department of Sociology, Western Reserve University, and to Miss Mildred Dorr, Family Health Association of Cleveland, for their invaluable assistance.
‡ *Marriage and Family Living*, pp. 71-74.

THE RESEARCH PROBLEM

In 1957, a study was conducted of the major social roles of a group of middle-aged parents living in the Cleveland metropolitan area whose children had permanently left the parental home. Specifically, an effort was made to discover if relationships between generational families (parents and their married child's family, the latter including the child, child's spouse, and grandchildren) were consistently related to behavior in particular social roles in middle-aged couples; and if middle-aged parents of two different social classes varied significantly in their patterns of social roles as a consequence of the leave-taking of children.

In this study middle-aged parents were defined as couples between the ages 45-60, whose children had married and permanently left the parental home. Generational families are those of the parents and their married child's family. The social roles studied were: parent, spouse, child of aging parents, worker, user of leisure time, church member, club or association member, citizen, friend, aunt or uncle, brother or sister.

THE SAMPLE

A complicated method was followed in an effort to obtain random samples of working-and middle-class families for study. Two separate two per cent random samples were drawn from the list of 12,000 marriages recorded in Cuyahoga County, Ohio, during 1956. Parents were then traced through these married couples, and an effort was made to secure an interview with the parents if they met the criteria of sample selection. These criteria were that the 1956 marriage was of the last child living at home, that the couple were white, and that both parents were between the ages of 45 and 60. Fifty-seven post-parental couples were located in this manner, and constitute the sample for this study.

For the 57 cases the median age of the wife was 53.4 and of the husband, 57.5. Ten of the husbands were in professional or technical occupations; 15 in managerial, office, or proprietary; 5 in clerical and sales; 13, craftsmen or foremen; 14, operatives and kindred workers. Thirty-three were identified as Protestant; 16,

Catholic; 7, Jewish; and 1, unknown. Forty-one per cent were natives of Cleveland, and over 75 per cent of the families had lived in the Cleveland area more than 10 years. Approximately one-half of the families represented West European and one-half East European nationality backgrounds. On the average each parental family had two married children. In some instances the last child had married as recently as eight months prior to the interview.

Data were obtained by interviewing one or both members of post-parental couple. Twenty-two interviews were conducted with both members of the couple present; the remaining 35, with the wife. The time of each interview varied from one and one-half to four hours.

The interviews included structured and semi-structured questions on patterns of inter-generational family continuity and social role behavior...

SOCIAL CLASS AND FAMILY CONTINUITY

The 57 cases were grouped by social class. Class assignments were made on the basis of Hollingshead's Index of Social Position (Hollingshead, 1949; 1954). This index is based upon two factors, occupation and level of education, with a given range of ISP scores representing a given social class. The five social classes delineated by Hollingshead have here been combined into three, with his classes I and II constituting our "upper"; his class III, our "middle"; and his classes IV and V, our "low."

A rating technique was developed to determine the degree of intergenerational family continuity, namely, a measure of the ongoing activities and interpersonal relationships of post-parental couples and their married child's family. The following eight factors were each rated on a three-point scale: 1) Feelings about children's marriage; 2) feelings about child-in-law; 3) closeness of family now; 4) children come for advice and take advice now; 5) family celebrations now; 6) visits between parents and children now; 7) communication between parents and children now; 8) help given to children now.

Scores (summations of the eight ratings) were assigned to one of four levels of family continuity: high, good, fair, or poor. (A fifth possibility, "no family continuity," did not occur in this sample.) The four levels were then grouped into two, "good to high" and "poor to fair"; 36 families were classified in the level called "high," and 21 in the "poor to fair" level, henceforth called "low."[1]

Social class was found to be inversely correlated with intergenerational family continuity. As shown in Table 1, the higher the class, the lower the continuity.

This finding that high intergenerational family continuity is positively correlated with low social class necessitates re-examination of a much beloved hypothesis, namely, that the higher the social class, the higher the family continuity. This does not mean that previous findings of high continuity among middle class families are to be rejected, but rather that there is need to explore this relationship by further empirical research.

CHANGES IN SOCIAL ROLES

Behavior in each of the 11 social roles mentioned earlier was examined for change since the leave-taking of the last married child from the parental home. A measure of role change was determined by examination of two behavioral items for each role. For instance, investigated under the parent role were changes in advice giving and receiving, and help and service exchanged between parents and children. A typical question was, "Some families help each other out in various ways. Have you happened to give help to your own parents, children, relatives or in-laws?" A similar question was asked about receiving help. The interviewer recorded the types of help exchanged before and since the leave-taking of children. The behavioral item was judged as "change" or "no change" after evaluation of the responses by the investigator.

Each of the other roles was examined in the same fashion with two behavioral items selected as sensitive indices for deter-

---

1. A second method of rating the interviews was used for checking the reliability of the scale. It provided criteria for the raters in judging the level of family continuity and was used initially by the investigator (Sussman, 1953). The correlation between the two methods was .99 by the Spearman rank correlation method.

mining role change. If a couple was reported as "change" on two behavioral items in a given role since the leave-taking of children, then "change" was recorded for that role.

As shown in Table 2, in four of the eleven social roles more than 50 per cent of the couples reported changes since the leave-taking of the last married child. These are the four roles of parent, spouse, user of leisure time, and church member. The frequency of 50 per cent of change in the sample was arbitrarily taken to indicate change in roles. When this measure was used, no significant changes were found to have taken place in the roles of worker, citizen, friend, child of aging parent, aunt or uncle, club or association member, or brother or sister.

Of the four role areas where changes were most frequent, significant differences by social class were found in the roles of spouse and user of leisure time. Significant differences were also found by family continuity levels for the spouse, leisure time, and church member roles.

A significantly higher proportion of couples with poor family continuity, as compared with those of high family continuity, reported changes in spouse roles. Change was in the direction of intensified inter-spousal activity. Couples reported spending more time together and doing more things with one another.

"Middle" and "upper" class parents indicated that spouse roles change before rather than after the marriage of the children. Most of these changes occurred when children went away from home to college. For these couples, the new inter-spousal pattern was well established by the time of the last child's marriage.

The higher the social class, the greater was the change in the role of user of leisure time.

The lower the family continuity, the greater was the change of the role of church member. The direction of change was to become more active in the church.

TABLE 1

INTERGENERATIONAL FAMILY CONTINUITY: BY SOCIAL CLASS

	Social Class		
Continuity Level	*High*	*Middle*	*Low*
Poor to Fair	16	12	8
Good to High	6	2	13

Chi Square 9.754, df 2; P < .01.

TABLE 2

NUMBER OF COUPLES WHO REPORTED CHANGES IN SOCIAL ROLES
AFTER LAST CHILD LEAVES HOME: BY SOCIAL CLASS.
AND BY INTERGENERATIONAL FAMILY CONTINUITY SCORES (N = 57)

	Number Who Changed				
Role	*Classes I & II* (N = 22)	*Class III* (N = 14)	*Classes IV & V* (N = 21)	*High Continuity* (N = 36)	*Low Continuity* (N = 21)
Parent...............	16	10	14	22	18
Spouse...............	11	13	13a	17	20b
User of leisure time......	16	9	4a	9	20b
Church member.........	14	9	12	15	20b
Child of aging parents....	4	2	4	6	4
Worker	7	3	3	6	7
Club or association member..............	8	4	6	12	6
Citizen...............	5	2	3	6	4
Friend...............	4	3	5	8	4
Aunt or uncle....	4	2	3	6	3
Brother or sister....... ..	6	5	5	9	7

a The differences between social classes are statistically significant at the .05 level.

b This difference between high and low continuity groups is significant at the .05 level.

DISCUSSION

Marriage of a child demands in both a legal and cultural sense that parental roles be redefined. Whether parents are ready or not, they are forced to modify the pattern of interpersonal relationships with their child and his new family. The spouse role is also expected to change quickly. The speed and nature of change is probably related to experience with the leave-taking of children from the family of orientation. If children have attended college, the changes in interpersonal relationships attendant upon the so-called "empty nest" may have begun to change at that time. The marriage of the last child is then the culmination of these changes.

Changes in spouse roles of post-parental couples were most significant among "middle" social class and low continuity families. "Upper" class families indicated that changes in spouse roles commenced during the early adolescence of their children. Many children were sent away to preparatory school and many parents began at that time to note changes in their relationship with one another. "Middle" class more than "lower" class parents indicated significant changes in spouse roles. In part these differences between "lower" and "middle" class couples can be explained by the high family continuity of the "lower" class and low continuity of the "middle" class families in this study.

Both husbands and wives experienced changes as users of leisure time. Substitutes for child-centered activities were those focused on reading, games at home, trips, driving out, hobbies, course taking, television viewing, and sports. Larger blocks of time were now available for home refurnishing, garden work, trips, longer vacations, and for "just loafing."

The "user of leisure time" role varied with social class and with family continuity level. The higher the social class the greater was the change in this role after the leave-taking of children. This change is related to social class values, financial means, and low family continuity. The higher social classes generally have internalized the value of a productive leisure, and with children no longer underfoot, they have the time and money to pursue the pleasures of leisure. In addition, as a group they spend less time with their married child's family than do persons of the lower classes. This fact has been empirically verified elsewhere (Seeley, 1956; Sussman, 1956). Moreover, more of the higher than lower class parents believed that leisure pursuits should be shared with friends of their own generation rather than with their child's family. It is also relevant that more of the "lower" than "middle" or "upper" class parents had children living in the Cleveland area with whom they could spend their leisure time.

Interest and activity in church may be a carry-over from the

Sunday School days of one's children. The change in the role of church member may also reflect the fact that many churches today carry on as many social as religious functions, and thus provide an acceptable channel for the expenditure of leisure time. The leave-taking of children may be the point at which church membership is more eagerly sought than before.

Increased church activity was highly correlated with low family continuity. This may be related to the failure of parents to establish satisfactory social relationships with their married child's family. Another contributory cause, already mentioned, is that a higher proportion of parents with high rather than low family continuity had relatives living within the Cleveland area. The social functions of religious organizations may be a substitute for the lack of social contacts with married children and their families.

The lack of change in worker, citizen, friend, and bilateral kin-related roles might have been anticipated, since these roles are not expected to change as a consequence of a child's marriage. As regards the worker role, for example, only a few of the middle-aged males in this sample changed their occupations or retired when they were relieved of supporting children. More often there was an intensification of work activity by the postparental male. Mothers more than fathers experienced radical changes in work roles. The interview did not contain questions for quantifying responses concerning changes in homemaker roles, but women respondents reported changes in meal planning, housekeeping, chore load, and shopping. Women now had more time for themselves and for their husbands.

Time is another factor affecting these findings. Some long-established roles may take more than eight months or a year to change, and the leave-taking period studied here may have been too short to test for change in those roles. Data on kin-related roles point to an ongoing network of interaction with nearby relatives that was established long before the leave-taking of children (Sussman, 1959). There are no empirical data to substantiate the belief that post-parental couples become more active than before in social relations with siblings and extended kin. Upon the leave-taking of children, social relations between parents and kin continue in the pre-leave-taking pattern.

Since only four of eleven roles studied showed significant changes in the post-parental period, it can be concluded that radical changes in the lives of parents do not occur immediately upon the leave-taking of children.

In three of the four social roles in which change occurred, differences by family continuity level were significant. In only two of these four were there significant social class differences. It would appear then that intergenerational family continuity is more important than the values and behavior associated with social class in affecting changes in the social roles of post-parental couples.

SUMMARY

Fifty-seven couples aged 45 to 60 were interviewed eight months or more after their last child had married and left the parental home. The couples were studied for the extent to which intergenerational family continuity was maintained, and the extent to which their behavior in each of nine social roles had changed since the leave-taking of the last child. Family continuity was found to be inversely related to social class. Half or more of the couples reported changes in the four roles of parent, spouse, user of leisure time, and church member; but changes in the roles of worker, sibling, child of aging parents, aunt or uncle, club or association member, citizen, or friend, were relatively infrequent. It appears that integenerational family continuity is a more important factor than social class in affecting changes in social roles among post-parental couples.

PERSONAL ADJUSTMENT IN THE
POSTPARENTAL PERIOD*‡

LELAND J. AXELSON, Ph.D.

THIS inquiry is a step toward exploring the so-called "empty-nest" period[1] of the family life cycle. Gravatt found that the research he reviewed emphasized "old age" and constituted inadequate material for the development of theories concerning the middle-age period.[2] For the purposes of this study, this sequence in family interrelationships is referred to as the *postparental period,* and is defined as that interval in the family life cycle when the children are no longer a regular physical member of the parent's home, but the parents have not entered that poorly defined period of "old age."

* Reprinted from: *Marriage and Family Living,* Vol. XXII, No. 1, February, 1960.

‡ The writer wishes to thank F. Ivan Nye for his material and theoretical assistance, and Joseph B. Perry, who cooperated in organizing and collecting the data. This is a condensation of a longer paper. Mimeographed copies of the entire manuscript may be obtained from the author.

1. Various authors have devised terms to designate this period of the family life cycle. "The Postparental Couple" is used by Ruth Cavan. *The American Family,* New York: Thomas Crowell Company, 1955, p. 573. Evelyn Duvall devotes a chapter to what she terms the "Middle Years," *Family Development,* New York: J. B. Lippincott Company, 1957, Chapter 13. See also pp. 376-78. Helen J. Hiltner refers to the period as "deserted parents" stage in "Changing Family Tasks of Adults," *Marriage and Family Living,* 15 (May, 1953), p. 112. Hiltner also recognizes our lack of knowledge in this area. Paul H. Landis uses the term the "empty-nest" stage, *Making the Most of Marriage,* New York: Appleton-Century-Crofts, Inc., 1955, p. 479. The "launching stage" is used in Willard Waller, *The Family, A Dynamic Interpretation,* New York: The Dryden Press, 1951, rev. ed., p. 425.

   James H. S. Bossard and Eleanor Boll, "Marital Unhappiness in the Life Cycle," *Marriage and Family Living,* 17 (February, 1955), pp. 13-14.

2. Arthur E. Gravatt, "Family Relations in Middle and Old Age, A Review," *Journal of Gerontology,* 8 (April, 1953), p. 200.

The general consensus among students of the postparental period suggests that mothers face severe adjustment problems due to the void in their daily interpersonal relationships which results from the physical departure of the children. Her source of stimulating experiences is further limited by a husband who devotes more time and energy to his occupation.[3]

Fathers in the postparental period are also thought to go through a period of personal maladjustment, although it is thought less traumatic than that of the mothers. It has been suggested by other writers that the men find their wives less attractive, fear loss of virility, and are depressed by mediocre occupational attainments.[4] Since various writers believe that a good deal of frustration and dissatisfaction with life in general is typical of this period, this inquiry has been directed toward the investigation of some of these ideas.

METHODOLOGY

The population consisted of men and women who had a child under twenty-five years of age marry between May 1, 1956, and April 30, 1958. The maximum age of twenty-five was chosen with the belief that as a child matures, he gradually reduces the interdependent relationships existing between himself and his parents, and marriage at a greater age would seem to be anti-climatic with respect to the problem at hand.

Wedding license applications made by persons residing in two medium sized communities located in the states of Washington and Idaho were checked for the names and addresses of their parents. A total of 696 individuals who gave their home addresses as one of these two communities used wedding certificates. Intensive efforts to locate all parents produced a total useable population of 390 fathers and 461 mothers.[5]

The data were collected by mailed questionnaire. A total return of 199 (51.0 per cent) useable father's questionnaire and

---

3. *Op. cit.*, Footnote 1.
4. *Ibid.*
5. An important source of the parents' names and mailing addresses was the local newspaper which serves these two communities and attempts to report all marriage ceremonies which concern individuals from the local area.

265 (57.7 per cent) useable mother's questionnaires was obtained. Census data indicate that the sample is not considerably biased in terms of occupations and educational attainment, although it could be unrepresentative in some other respect.

Definitions. For the purposes of this analysis, the respondents were divided into two categories — those still having one or more single children under eighteen years of age remaining at home and those respondents who have no single children under eighteen years of age remaining at home. Those individuals with single children under eighteen years of age remaining at home are referred to as the quasi-postparental group, and the parents with no single child under eighteen remaining at home are designated as the true postparental group.

THE FINDINGS

Conceptually, the decreased interpersonal relationships and the increasing personal dissatisfaction which supposedly results during this period should be exhibited in dissatisfaction with daily living. With this thought in mind, the mothers and fathers were asked to indicate their present degree of satisfaction in the seven basic life areas involving family income, house and furniture, recreation, relationships to children, relationships to spouse, daily work, and the community as a place to live. The individuals considered satisfied were those responding either entirely or generally satisfied, and the individuals considered dissatisfied were those responding either entirely or somewhat dissatisfied or fairly well satisfied.

Differences in satisfaction between the two postparental groups for both men and women were statistically nonsignificant. Sixty-one and six-tenths per cent of the women in the quasi-postparental period indicated they are satisfied with these seven life areas, while 62.4 per cent of the women in the true postparental period indicated satisfaction. The men in the quasi-postparental period show a similar adjustment with 61.8 per cent responding satisfied, and the men in the true postparental period indicated that they are 65.4 per cent satisfied. The greatest amount of satisfaction was shown by both groups with their interpersonal relationships, and the least satisfaction indicated was with income.

In an earlier study, the same life satisfaction items were included in a questionnaire administered to women with children in the first and tenth grades. From this sample, data were extracted for two additional groups of respondents. One group of 281 mothers had children who were twelve years of age or younger, the second group of 239 women had children who were thirteen years of age or older. The satisfaction indicated by these groups of women is 59.9 and 57.9 per cent, respectively. The data from mothers in the child-rearing stage lend support to the conclusion that *no significant difference* in satisfaction in these seven basic life areas occurs as mothers move into the post-parental period.

The second aspect of this inquiry attempts to discover longitudinal differences in several life areas. This was accomplished by asking the respondents to think back to the time their child was of high school age, and to note if changes had taken place.[6] See Table I for a partial list of the items investigated.

The pattern of responses to these questions reveals a general and in four items a significant *increase in satisfaction* with the interpersonal and financial aspects of daily living. Significant decreases occur in the concern for the child's welfare by women in both stages of the postparental period. (See Table I.) Financial worries have decreased significantly for the mothers of the true postparental period, while financial worries for the mothers of the quasi-postparental period have only begun to decrease. Women in both stages of the postparental period indicate important increases in satisfaction with their marital adjustment and the activities they share with their husbands. A nonsignificant trend toward more interest in their daily work was recorded by women of both groups.[7]

6. Sociologists, in general, have been skeptical of recall material, contending that respondents will tend to use more optimistic statements. The results of the inquiry would seem to indicate that this is not the case here.

7. An additional attempt was made to obtain some information from the mothers who did not respond to the original questionnaire. Questions concerning changes since the child was in high school were selected from the questionnaire and sent to the nonrespondents. From a small return of 13 per cent, no appreciable differences in change were found to exist between these respondents and the mothers included in the original group of respondents.

A significant *increase* in loneliness was recorded by the women in the true postparental period. The significant decrease in community activities indicated by the mothers may explain, in part, their increasing loneliness.

When viewing their lives in retrospect, the fathers indicate that significant positive changes in the area of concern for the child's welfare, financial worries, activities with the wife, marital adjustment, and interest in occupation have taken place since the child was in high school. The trend is for the men to be less concerned with their own health. (See Table I.)

CONCLUSIONS

This investigation has been an attempt to test empirically some of the speculation concerning the postparental period. Contrary to what several writers in the field have hypothesized, this period of life seems as satisfying as earlier periods.

Contrary to the general findings, women indicated a tendency toward concern about their health and a greater need for outside contacts. For mothers in the true postparental period, a significant increase in loneliness also was found.

TABLE I

CHANGES IN SELECTED LIFE AREAS REPORTED BY WOMEN AND MEN
SINCE CHILD WAS IN HIGH SCHOOL — PER CENT DISTRIBUTION

Area	Group	Women More now	Less now	t	N	Men More now	Less now	t	N
Concern for	A	11.4	37.4	3.59**	123	15.7	27.5	1.43	102
child's welfare	B	12.5	51.0	4.04**	96	12.4	34.8	2.49*	89
Part in commu-	A	7.0	23.5	2.44*	115	5.8	14.6	0.57	103 } *
nity activities	B	5.5	35.2	3.24**	91	6.7	29.2	3.12*	89
Financial worries	A	13.3	25.0	1.62	120 } **	16.7	22.5	0.49	102 } *
	B	5.4	52.2	4.95**	92	7.9	40.4	3.59**	89
Loneliness	A	14.7	7.8	1.16	116 } **	8.2	15.5	1.25	97
	B	31.8	11.4	2.32*	88	18.6	10.5	1.07	86
Activities with	A	24.8	5.8	2.91**	121	32.0	7.8	3.08**	103
husband or wife	B	37.6	2.2	4.28**	93	40.2	12.6	2.92**	87
Satisfaction with	A	21.1	2.6	3.26**	114	25.0	2.0	3.36**	100
marital adjust.	B	25.6	3.5	2.89**	86	23.0	4.6	2.48**	87
Interest in	A	11.6	6.3	0.30	112	21.8	3.0	2.87**	101
daily work	B	15.2	9.8	0.78	92	15.5	9.5	0.84	84

NOTE: A=quasi-postparental group, B=true postparental group. t tests proportional differences between the more and less responses within the same group. Chi-square is used to compare differences between groups A and B.
  * Significant at the 5 per cent level.
  ** Significant at the 1 per cent level.

It has been suggested by others that increased mental illness results from this period. Recent census figures reveal that the greatest number of first admissions to public hospitals for mental disease in the United States occurs between the ages of 35-44 for men and 25-34 for women[8] — much too early for the postparental period to have had an influence. Between the ages of 45-54, the first admission rates *decreased* by 15.5 per cent for men and 25.0 per cent for women. This decline is considerably greater than the expected decline in total population due to death. These data coupled with the findings of this report seriously question the assumed correlation between mental disorders and the postparental period.

---

8. U. S. Bureau of the Census, *Statistical Abstract of the United States:* 1958 (Seventy-ninth edition.), Washington, D.C., 1958, p. 82.

ROUGHLY FIFTY*

ANN LEIGHTON

LET'S see," said a gallant college contemporary, who might be expected to know exactly. "Let's see — how old are you now — roughly fifty?"

So that is it. At forty-nine, if one is female and American, one begins to be roughly fifty. And so one, presumably, remains until one breaks one's hip at ninety. An American woman's age is marked by no convenient milestones. At sixteen, she is sweet; at forty, fair and fat; and after that, roughly fifty, as it were, forever.

Not that she herself has ever been one to avoid milestones. The mere fact of attaining fifty has long been shimmering in her sight like the towers of Chartres Cathedral to pilgrims across the flat wheatlands. When I arrive at that haven, she has thought, there will be a reawakening. Early promises can be fulfilled. She will be allowed, and even expected, to pick up all the threads left dangling so invitingly in her youth, when she plunged suddenly into domesticity. Free at last in both time and spirit, eager — now her family is raised — to make her personal contribution to her country's way of life, what is not open to her?

When she first happily announced herself as "middle-aged" and found that it is the one thing American women never are, she began to discover the anomalies of her new existence. Even the word matron is denied her. It is a poison word now, like empire and cartel. Matrons rejoice with maids in happy hymns, but editors write, "Do we have to use that damn word? It's so stuffy." So, roughly fifty it is. But, even after these warnings, it comes as a shock to the average American college-bred woman

---

* *The Atlantic Monthly, 189:* 53-54, June 1952.

— who has been anticipating her shift from the domestic squirrel wheel to what she still considers "real" life — to discover finally that, for her, roughly fifty equals zero.

Perhaps it all started with the complete disappearance of grandmothers — those charming creatures who rustled softly, smelled sweet, wore little caps, and doled out peppermints. The next to begin to disappear was the full-blown, obviously middle-aged woman. Only buds, in various stages of tightness, were allowed. If they began to open out, remedies were found to close them up again, the way florists manage with wax at the base of petals to give even the oldest blooms a fresh, opening air. For the woman who insisted upon looking her age there was not even an appropriate costume — only styles affected by the very young. Forever dirndls — until she broke that hip and got a shawl, from the attic.

The phenomenon of American society discarding its educated middle-aged women as soon as they are free agents has been noted by anthropologists. Even the most casual observers realize that middle-aged women in America are, as such, somehow taboo. None of the great industries, which exist solely for and by the little woman who holds the purse strings, can see her for dust after she exceeds the age and mentality of a child bride. As in the dress trade, so in advertising, the American woman leaps straight from the exuberant young shopper to the jolly ancient at the garden gate. Cosmetic manufacturers have lowered their norms from schoolgirls to babies; their only attention to the frankly aging woman is a blue rinse. And on television and radio and in the illustrated magazines the middle-aged woman exists merely as a prop to be cried upon in soap operas by the ever young sufferers, or as a joke in cartoons of self-indulgent, egg-shaped clubwomen baffled by treasurer's reports, or as a menace, in serious articles where the middle-aged woman is always a Mom. A prop, a joke, a menace. Secretly many may sympathize with the Moms — at least they have discovered a mode of survival.

Everywhere outside America in the world today, the independent middle-aged woman, freed from family responsibilities, is reabsorbed by the national life. True, the Hindus used to burn widows, which was at least a frank admission of the problem. But the British put a stop to it. The British hate waste and have always found middle-aged women useful. And at best it was rather barbaric — so unlike the modern American custom of telling the average middle-aged woman just to go away and amuse herself at anything as long as it has nothing to do with what is really going on. The conception of a hobby as the thing to keep educated women from doing anything useful is entirely new and American.

Denied her bright and final future, the hobby-resister still resolves that she will not be caught struggling in a "plight." When that chloroform pad to stop all protests is produced, it is better just to lie back, breathe deeply, and give up, clasping one's hobby.

Though, of course, instead of a hobby, there are lots and lots of things for the middle-aged woman to do that everyone wants her to do. Nothing really paying, except in its own reward, but that is what she has been working for up to now anyway. Most of the things she is welcome to do are a continuation of all the things she has been doing, only now the field is wider. She can support more than one church, and any number of charities. She can baby-sit to eternity. She can listen all day to quiz programs and wait for her telephone to ring. Who complains that middle-aged women have no opportunities!

And, naturally, if she ever got started in anything "real" before marriage, she can try to get back into that again, and very likely she will be let in, on the fringes, sitting at a reception desk, or keeping files, or hiring others to do what she wants to do herself. It won't be what she might have had if she had combined a career with marriage, but it will be as good as the old soldiers in England dressed up as Beefeaters and set to guard the Crown Jewels behind bars in the Tower of London. It will feel rather like that, too.

But if, encouraged by a national crisis and manpower shortage, the middle-aged women who have made a success of their families and would now like to have a try at making a success of something else, actually think they have anything to offer their country beyond knitting, they *have* to be disabused. Statistically they may be the hardiest, most intelligent and reliable group that could be drawn upon, with fewer personal commitments and a greater eagerness to be used, but actually the whole idea of using them at all is un-American. For them, Hobby is the only watchword.

And what a host of hobbies there are to choose from! There are those timeless ones of collecting things — all the things no one wants until, perhaps, they are ranged out, mile upon mile, on shelves. And there are the hobbies of making things — such unexpected things out of such unlikely materials that it is almost impossible to tell the Before from the After. And there are those purely original and creative hobbies when one does things one never dreamed one could — like children in a progressive school — sculpture and paintings executed in such innocence of design and technique as to look like those lovely things done by savages. And for the really scholarly, there are studies — Russian, for instance — not that they will ever be allowed to use it. The only stipulation about hobbies is that they, like middle-aged women, stay one remove from reality or usefulness. For instance, carving is recommended, but not building a house. Perhaps it is considered too constructive. American society protects its women.

Is that, then, the trouble? American middle-aged women do not want to be protected? Cannot feel that hobbies are more than thumb-twiddling? That is simply faulty adaptation and easily dealt with. The woman in such a state of mind can go to a summer school run by her Alma Mater for just such as she, and there she can learn, as they put it, "to come to terms with herself" as no one else seems to want to. And if she feels still at a loss, she can go to an analyst who will dig and delve and come up with something that attracted her as a very young girl and that will be suggested as the interest for the rest of her life. And if she still thinks she could make a contribution to the national life along a line for which she was trained in college — if she cannot realize the total destruction involved in raising a family

— then she will have to go to one of those nice sanitariums where she can take up any number of quieting occupations in none of which she ever had any interest at all.

At least, she thinks, among her peers in the sanitarium, we *can* think. If the new educators of women reduce education to what will be immediately useful after graduation, the sanitariums will be quite dull when those girls reach middle age. At least now the ladies can discuss dear old Proust and Joyce and re- member how they resolved to keep ahead of their children in- tellectually and never let themselves become a burden or a bore, and even distinguish themselves in some other than do- mestic ways after the children were grown.

How amusing to think one could be worth anything after devoting oneself to one's family!

Oblivion? Nonsense. Hobbyland!

Oh, do you like this pattern? I am *so* glad. I've made a thou- sand . . .

LETTERS TO AND FROM THE EDITOR

Sir:

I have just finished reading "Roughly Fifty" by Ann Leighton in the June *Atlantic,* and all I can say is "Me too." What an empty life after those busy and happy years when one was al- most dizzy and breathless from trying to get into each day all that needed to be done.

But to be a good wife, mother, and homemaker is just no qualification for a real working career after the battle has been fought and won. I am the mother of three children who have made a success of both their personal and public lives and now have homes and families of their own. The "nest is empty," to put it in a sentimental way. Not even a husband to keep the home fires burning, for he decided that he too wanted freedom and flitted away to, shall I say, greener pastures.

I have tried unsuccessfully to find some work to bring in an income and, of course, to keep me busy and interested, but al- ways the answer is the same, "No experience." Yes, I could

baby-sit and sell magazines from door to door, or read to in-
valids, or what have you. Certainly they want us to be volunteers
in the hospitals and take one day a week at the Thrift Shop,
for sweet charity's sake, or head up the committee for the bazaar
for the church — anything but a paid job that will assure one of
a feeling of independence and security. Having tried all the
above activities, I know whereof I speak, and perhaps, like Mrs.
Leighton, I am disgusted.

There are two things I should like to happen in the near
future: first, a uniform divorce law in our country, and then
some recognition of women as individuals with potential power
to be utilized, in a really constructive manner.

My father tells me that age is not a question of calendar years,
but of one's own mental ability. But the accent today is on
youth, and so the young men fight the wars and the young wom-
en get the jobs, while we are supposed to take care of the children and cook the meals — which frankly I do not want to do
any more, since, like a good soldier, I did my stretch at that,
and now want a change, or at least a chance to try my hand
and mind at another sort of life.

I am at present in the process of trying my luck at taking in
roomers, to keep the wolf from the door, and I therefore shall
find myself at the same old stand, making beds and chasing
dust and cobwebs, when I would so much rather be chasing
rainbows, and maybe finding the pot of gold. But "woman's place
is in the home," and that is where they are going to try to
keep us.

Well, I suppose we will keep on struggling to find the answer.
And I surely hope Mrs. Leighton will write more articles
along this line.

Unfortunately I have not had a college training, although my
family wanted me to, but I elected to be married, and from that
experience have come my three wonderful children. But why, at
the culmination of all the happy years together, does a husband
decide to run off and try for something new and different?

Are we each and all living in a transition age, full of restless-
ness, and unable to come to grips with reality in our life of

today? What about our moral values — are they changing and are we older women going to be able to adjust to the change?

Ten years ago I thought I knew all the answers, but now I know how little I know.

My three children are like Mrs. Leighton's — two boys and a girl; all through college and in homes of their own; so you see I am older than Mrs. Leighton and further along the road to nowhere.

E.D.

Sir:

Mrs. Leighton sounds like someone who expects to find the professional world waiting with open arms to welcome her, and this after years of having done nothing to justify confidence in herself. It is hardly realistic for her to expect to step into a position of responsibility on the basis of the promise she may have shown when she was twenty. The standards of many of our professions would suffer severely if all the middle-aged women who once had responsible careers suddenly stepped into the positions they left, as if nothing had changed in the fifteen or twenty years intervening.

A middle-aged woman of intelligence and education who has a real contribution to make will always find places in society where her talents are needed. It may take some effort, ingenuity, and imagination, but in any case the mountain will certainly not come to Mahomet.

Mrs. Carolyn Lipetz
Ithaca, N.Y.

Sir:

How many people have enough money to just sit back and do what they really want to do at age fifty?

For that matter, how many men do what they want, at fifty or any other age?

Mrs. Burton A. Lehman
Beaufort, N.C.

Sir:

If Mrs. Leighton is in or approaching the fiftyish age and is fortunate enough to have her husband, what is her dilemma? Certainly when she chose him for a life partner, she didn't think then that he wouldn't be alive when she herself reached the middle of the road. So, if the old man is still around, what's wrong — for Mrs. Leighton and the thousands of other women who admit to the same problem — about concentrating on him?

Mrs. Thomas Waller
Fort Salonga, N.Y.

Sir:

Simple curiosity impels me to ask the location of the ivory tower in which Ann Leighton is being forced to waste her declining years.

And who, exactly, are the mysterious "they" who are so effectually preventing her from realizing her mid-century potentialities for achievement? A council of stern town elders? Or a hide-bound husband, perhaps, some stiff-necked relic of the Victorian Era?

I have never been aware that "permission" from any authority on earth was a prerequisite to accomplishment, for male or female of any vintage. Rather, it is always an end result of talent, intelligence, energy, ambition, and plain hard work.

Wailing self-pity, such as that in which Mrs. Leighton is indulging is definitely no substitute for a realistic appraisal of her situation, plus a goodly measure of "drive."

At thirty-two I'm looking forward to great possibilities for personal accomplishment when I shall find myself roughly forty, or fifty — or even roughly a hundred.

Vera G. Kinsler
Cleveland Heights, Ohio

Sir:

Ann Leighton's pathetic statement of the plight of the middle-aged American woman moves me to ask her if she has ever been an active member of the League of Women Voters.

I cannot believe that a woman of her caliber is unable to find a fulltime paying job, if that is what she wants.

If not, there is no need for her to resort to the kind of hobby that "stays one remove from reality" and is "designed to keep educated women from doing anything useful."

Please, Mrs. Leighton, before you settle down in the sanitarium with your Proust and your knitting, look up your local League of Women Voters and find out what goes on.

Eleanor N. Lewis
Baltimore, Md.

STRESSES IN MIDDLE LIFE FROM THE PSYCHIATRIST'S VIEWPOINT*

LLOYD JAMES THOMPSON, M.D.

BEFORE discussing stress, I should like to inquire briefly as to what we mean by middle-aged. I once absorbed a definition of a middle-aged person as anyone ten years older than you are. When I was in the eighth grade, I am sure I thought a college football player was middle-aged. When I was 30 I put people of 50 in that category, but now I find I have put the age up again. To keep an objective approach, let our pivotal point for middle age be put at somewhere around 50.

WHAT IS STRESS?

Now, what about the meaning of this word stress? It is an old word and has come to have many meanings for many people. Engineers have used the word for a long time with a technical connotation. During World War II, it was brought into our diagnoses when we spoke about precipitating stress in relation to combat exhaustion. Since then, Hans Selye has done the most to make stress an important term in biology and medicine, but it seems to me that Selye's own definition has changed from time to time since he first started writing about it.

At a recent meeting of the Southern Research Council at Duke University, the eight members of a panel were asked for a definition of the word stress. Of course, there was general agreement but no two of them saw eye to eye in all aspects.

One might ask, does any disturbance of homeostasis mean stress? Surely not, for if true homeostasis is ever established, it cannot last for more than a minute or two. Thus, we can hardly say how much stress exists and how much stress must be present

---

* *Geriatrics, 10*: 162-164, April 1955.

to produce an abnormal deviation from homeostasis. So let me propose that what is stress to one person may be only a challenge with fun and exhilaration for another person. Also, what is stress in one family, community, nation, or society may not have the same qualitative or quantitative significance elsewhere. Perhaps even more important is recognition that what is stress in infancy or adolescence may not be of much concern in middle age or later on, and vice versa.

PSYCHOLOGIC STRESSES OF THE MENOPAUSE

Stresses of middle life, if viewed from the standpoint of the psychiatrist, seems to focus naturally on the individual. Just as naturally, we must go beyond the individual to the family, the community, and other groups within his milieu. It seems natural to consider women's problems first, because here women are subject to a definite biologic stress during middle life. The terms applied to this period — change of life, the menopause, the involution — are all fraught with rather ominous meaning. To men and women alike, they signify an end to sex desire and responsiveness, with less interest in maintaining a well-groomed, attractive appearance.

Now, what actually takes place biologically is a gradual failure of certain ovarian functions, the exhaustion of the primordial follicles, and a gradually increasing estrogen deficit. This deprivation producing an imbalance which results in a rise of the pituitary gonadotropins is an accepted fact. I shall not go beyond that.

According to Novack, writing on the menopause in the October 1954 *Journal of the American Medical Association*, the only clear-cut symptoms of estrogen deprivation are the vasomotor symptoms, such as flushes, sweats, and hot tingling flashes. He believes that such symptoms as headache, vertigo, fatigue, arthralgias, nervousness, and irritability are probably more often functional in origin. Note he doesn't say "always," but "probably more often functional in origin." Even today, women often feel that the menopause is inevitably followed by insanity, obesity, cancer, cessation of sex life, and hirsutism. I am in agreement with Novack. I would say that perhaps all these things are true, but there are certainly other sources of stress that can be added from the case records of the psychiatrist's office as well as from the records of the general practitioner.

First of all, for the unmarried career woman, any birthday beyond the fortieth may add conflictual stress concerning her role as a woman in competition with men, concerning her professional status with younger people coming on, and concerning her aloneness and financial security. For the unmarried woman who has stayed behind to maintain the old home, not only to help the parents but to free other siblings, the stresses from conscious and unconscious conflict are too numerous to mention.

In the ordinary course of events, married women also face many problems provocative of stress, especially after they have reached their late forties. In the majority of instances, regardless of high divorce rates and childless marriages, the average woman has as her job in life that of being a wife, mother, and housekeeper. Just as middle age begins, she is called upon to give up in large part her satisfying job, especially her role as mother. Her husband, if successful, is probably immersed in professional activities that are somewhat beyond her ken. The children should be out by this time and established in homes of their own, but she may then be in the position to hold on to her grandchildren, even vicariously. Of course, she can continue to cook and sweep and make beds, and is it any wonder then that she tries to hold onto her job? If the man of the family had to give up his grocery store, his law practice, or his merit-system job at 45, he too would hang on for dear life.

One other aspect of the married woman's situation, that Dr. Stieglitz has already pointed out, is that she should consider the probability that she will sooner or later be a widow.

THE PSYCHOLOGIC STRESSES OF THE MIDDLE-AGED MAN

Turning to the male of the species, I am confident that men do not have a physiologic menopause analogous to that of the female. It certainly is true that man in the same period of life, may have depressive reactions exactly like those of the involutional melancholia occurring in women. Men experience about the same amount of stresses, but the stresses are different in origin.

The very successful man of 50 may have accumulated so much money, have so many obligations, and hold so many offices and committee memberships, that he cannot stop the pyramiding process when he wants to get away from it — even when myocardial infarction occurs.

The moderately successful man may be goaded by his own ego drive or by a frustrated wife toward greater and greater accomplishments as the time grows shorter. It is in this group that we see, at middle age, definite anxieties about a son, or a symbolic son in the person of a younger partner who may threaten to displace him. Simultaneously his wife may notice that many of her personal ideals are beginning to be realized through a son — those ideals which had not been realized through her husband. Now, the man's own unresolved conflicts with his parents may make him vulnerable in his role as an elder, and toleration of younger men as business rivals and persons in the family constellation may also be a cause of stress.

In the man of mediocre accomplishment we may find a repetitious girding of the loins to go forth and show the world, or at least his wife and family, that he is someone after all. Failing in direct result, he may find another woman who seems to understand his frustrations and his unrecognized partial success, which only adds, of course, to the stress at this time of life. It is not only to the man of mediocre success that this may happen.

Going beyond questions of success, finances, career, or community standing, we should recognize that for the middle-aged man his sexual adjustment is a likely source of stress which may be completely hidden even from wife and family doctor.

A man's ego strength, in contrast to that of a woman, depends so much on his sexual potency. At the age of 50, he will admit freely that he cannot play the game of tennis or handball that he used to, but at the first manifestation of lessened potency, he may become distraught and quickly develop a gnawing feeling that somehow he is not the man he should be. He may continue as a successful president of his bank or he may redouble his enterprises in various ways as a compensation, all the while keeping his phallic stress to himself.

Menopausal women, anticipating a falling off of libido, may be surprised that, with the fear of pregnancy gone, flames are rekindled. They are ashamed of it sometimes, and if the husband has begun to lose interest and his potency is not what it used to be, that too can be a source of stress and anxiety in the sexual field.

It should be mentioned that obesity also may become a psychiatric problem in middle life. It is psychiatric in that so much of the middle-aged spread is due to overeating and the overeating in both men and women may be a symptom of stress, of frustration, and an effort to gain some sort of satisfaction.

EDUCATION FOR MATURITY A LIFELONG PROCESS

Going beyond the individual man or women, we find that society in general fosters a rather dismal outlook for the middle-aged person and thereby increases his stress. Studies have been made by Landis, Tuckerman, and Feifel that bear out this statement. Feifel says there is little doubt concerning the need for an educational program to train people for adjustment to old age. This program should have the broad aim of anticipating and preventing the anxieties and maladjustments attendant on growing old.

It seems to me that any such educational program should not wait tacitly until middle life, but should be a continuing health measure from the time of conception onward. The way in which a person meets the stresses of middle life and old age depends not so much upon physiologic changes as upon the shaping of the personality in earlier years by the family, the community, and the general culture. The development of social emotional maturity insuring full enjoyment of old age really starts at the beginning of life.

EMOTIONAL CONFLICTS OF THE MIDDLE-AGED MAN*

OTTO BILLIG, M.D. and ROBERT W. ADAMS, JR., M.D.

MIDLIFE should bring to the successful man recognition and satisfaction. He has prepared himself for years to obtain a secure position in his community and to find acceptance in his job and profession. He has gained experience and laid the groundwork to his success. By now, he should have reached the peak of his accomplishments. However, this is often not the case. There has been an increasing awareness that the period of middle age can bring anxiety and insecurity. We have pointed out this problem in previous papers.[1,2] There have also been other publications by Bergler[3] and Meerloo[4] on this subject.

CLINICAL STUDY

Our own studies are based on material gained from two groups with different socioeconomic standards. The subjects in the low socioeconomic group were miners living in isolated rural communities. Of the 150 cases studied, approximately 100 were in the age group between 35 and 55 years. All were admitted to Vanderbilt Hospital for persistent, incapacitating illness that had not responded to previous therapy. Fifty-five per cent had clear-cut emotional illness, either anxiety or conversion states. Approximately 33 per cent had some form of psychosomatic illness, such as allergies and peptic ulcers, and only 15 per cent suffered from definite organic diseases without emotional factors involved.

The other group examined had a middle-class socioeconomic background with adequate financial security.

The case histories of the first group were stereotyped. They

* *Geriatrics, 12:* 535-541, September 1957.

came from isolated rural areas where they found little emotional satisfaction. Almost no recreational activities were available in the community. The families seldom went to town, and visited but little. Most of their free time was devoted to a strict church. The typical father of this group was a rigid, austere person who had little to say, but who ruled his house with "an iron hand." The mother took care of the usually large family and had little time for individual members. She very often felt overwhelmed by her responsibilities and showed a tendency to neurotic complaints. Little affection was shown in the home.

Emotional difficulties manifested themselves early in life and took the form of neuropathic traits, such as enuresis, abnormal fears, nail biting, and sleepwalking. Many of the patients did not finish grade school; they often stopped going to school when about 12 or 13 years old, and started to work in the mines. Some manifested behavior difficulties during adolescence, and a fairly large percentage of the patients started to drink in their late teens. They married at an early age and, for several years following marriage, did not pay much attention to their wives, but were "running around with the boys." Several children were born in quick succession.

During their late 20's or early 30's, a behavior change was noticed. The young men started to work more regularly; they complained of being tired when they came home from work; they became increasingly health conscious and preoccupied with their physical condition. Very often, a minor illness or accident precipitated a condition of incapacity. The clinical symptoms manifested themselves between the ages of about 35 to 45 years.

The family relationship showed many difficulties between father and son. The fathers made great demands on their sons, creating a feeling of emotional insecurity. The young boys felt unaccepted, and their insecurities resulted in neuropathic traits early in life. A great deal of resentment was felt toward the father. The mother was unable to give them the proper emotional support because of her own feelings of inadequacy. She often felt that the demands made upon her were beyond her capacities. Based upon that feeling of insecurity in relationship to the father, the boy *unconsciously* resented the father, expressing this in the form of aggressive behavior and hostility aimed against all authority. This group, seemingly because of its cultural limitations, started to age sooner and reached middle age in earlier years than men in areas less restricted culturally. Upon entering middle age, these men displayed outspoken response to minor precipitating factors, such as minor accidents or illnesses.

DIFFICULTIES IN FATHER-SON RELATIONSHIP

In other cultural groups, the problem of conflict between father and son may show some variation but the basic conflict seems to be essentially the same. This is illustrated in the following history.

Case History

A successful business man of 44 showed increasing body concern during the previous two or three years. He became alarmed about his heart and particularly about his bowel functions. He visited a number of doctors who examined him thoroughly, and he was always told that he was organically healthy. The patient never fully trusted his doctors and became concerned whenever a laboratory test was repeated. He immediately concluded there was something seriously wrong with him and panicked. Not believing his doctors, he changed them frequently. When he was told that amebic dysentery was suspected, he became extremely concerned and alarmed about his condition. Panic states persisted. He complained of continuous heart palpitations and other cardiac symptoms and was completely incapacitated. The patient was referred for psychiatric examination and treatment, which was difficult for him to accept.

The past history revealed that his father was a successful businessman who worked very hard, spending many hours at his place of business. He worked every day including Sundays. His employees and his son feared his violent temper. He was unable to tolerate opposition and was amazed if anyone questioned his authority. He was strict and demanded complete adherence from family and employees.

The patient was an only son. As a child, he saw little of

his father, for the father never had time for him or other members of the family. When the patient was 7 or 8 years old, he was not allowed to play with other children, but had to tend to chores around the house. He wanted a bicycle and, later on, a motor scooter, but the father opposed such "nonsense," although the family could well afford them. At first, the patient thought that his father considered it "spoiling;" but he realized, as he grew older, that his father was afraid he might be hurt in an accident.

When our patient finished high school, his father decided that he should enter an engineering school. As a student, he had difficulty making his grades, although he was obviously intellectually capable of doing so. He failed and had to drop out of college. He entered his father's business on the latter's insistence. The father was unable to delegate any authority to his son or to any of the other workers. He praised only rarely; approval came only when all orders were carried out to his complete satisfaction. He would often check with the patient at one to three o'clock in the morning to see if everything was done according to his instructions. The father insisted that his son accompany him to the office on Sundays, although the plant was closed.

The father died at 68 when the patient was 29. The son took over the business, but felt insecure about assuming authority. The older workers kept reminding him that "the old man did things so-and-so," and the patient resented their attitude. When they became older, their reduced productivity disturbed him out of all proportion. He could not bring himself to either retire them or to add some additional workers. Although he had had no previous trouble making decisions, he became increasingly indecisive.

He was not able to talk very much about his mother or the mother's role. After a long period, he was able to describe her as "not an outstanding woman." She complained a great deal about her difficulties; she was not able to oppose the father in any of his wishes; and the patient resented her lack of support in dealing with the father. He was financially dependent on his father and uncertain whether his meager income would be sufficient to support him and his wife. He could not bring himself to look for a better paying job, since he was certain of his father's disapproval. The young man delayed telling his father about his intentions to marry as long as he could. As he expected, the father objected to his plans at first, but finally assented.

The young wife was a shy, insecure woman of 20, who had difficulty in expressing her affection. This was later interpreted as lack of affection by the patient. Because he felt unwanted, he became critical and nagged his wife about many minor things. When she become impatient and quarrels developed, his feeling or rejection was reinforced. He expressed his attitude by saying, "Nobody gives a hang about me," and had fantasies of leaving home.

They had three children, with the oldest, a son, born a year after the marriage. The patient was apprehensive over his wife's becoming "pregnant so soon," and did not want the child, but soon after the child was born, he became very solicitous toward his son and wanted to give him all the things he had missed. Particularly obvious, for example, was his desire to give his son a motor scooter when the boy was only 11 and had not shown any interest in a scooter.

Discussion

This patient had shown considerable insecurity in his life development. He felt he was not accepted by his father and strongly resented the father's demands upon him. He felt increasingly rejected by the mother because of her inability to take any definite stand in the family affairs. These experiences colored his later attitudes.

The patient unconsciously chose a wife with characteristics similar to those of his mother, and later in the marriage, he felt that the emotional climate was the same as in his parent's home. He tested his relationship to his wife until he found a point where she rejected him and thus considered his feeling a rejection justified.

He felt insecure about his relationship to men, and found it necessary to defend himself against older men throughout his life. When he was put in any position of authority, he became critical of older men and wanted to eliminate them. He recognized that minor inefficiencies often disturbed him "unreasonably." The resulting guilt feelings motivated him to establish a retirement program in his plant.

His insecurity in his relationship to his father made it impossible for him to identify himself with an adequate father's role. When his wife became pregnant, he could not accept the pregnancy because of his "financial worries." After the son was born, he had to deny the unwanted pregnancy and the only protection he could find was by identifying himself with the son rather than accepting the role of father. It furnished satisfaction for what he had missed as a boy. He gave the boy all the toys he himself had wanted as a child. When the son reached maturity, he manifested neurotic difficulties in the form of anxiety and somatic complaints.

Our studies of other middle-aged men showed similar reaction patterns. Apparently, the patient's relationship with his father greatly influences his adjustments to his children. Remaining, unresolved conflicts toward the father created strong feelings of resentment and hostility. The child represses his fantasies because of his fear of an overpowering and successful father, but the underlying resentment remains. Older men continue to be a target for his feelings of hostility.

When he becomes a father himself, these repressed feelings are mobilized. Being unconsciously aware of such hostile feelings between father and son, he resents the unborn child and develops apprehensions at the time of the son's birth.

Recent studies of "expectant fathers" revealed definite emotional problems in about 60 per cent of the cases studied.[5] The author concludes that those fathers are unable to accept the pregnancy of their wives.

Our case history deals with a man who became psychotic at the time of his son's birth. This problem has found a great deal of attention in the Oedipus complex, according to which the son develops feelings of hostility for the father and fantasies of destroying the father when the father reaches middle age.

In our study, we are concerned with this problem from the father's, rather than the son's, point of view. What happens to such a man at middle age when he believes that his son resents him? The recognition of such problems is nothing new. Many primitive tribes have religious taboos in which they attempt to protect themselves from any hostile impulses against their unborn children. The taboo requires that they remain completely inactive at the time of the child's birth. Any form of activity at such periods is considered harmful to the child, and protection is given through the complete inactivity of the father. If the father violates the taboo, he has to pay penance.

OVEREMPHASIS ON COMPETITION

Today's social structure seems to be particularly conducive to the development of tensions and insecurities.[2] An overemphasis on competition reinforces already existing uncertainties. The constant fear of being replaced may appear. In order to convince themselves of their continued success, such individuals have to constantly find new proof in other competitive areas. Business success then becomes based on outdoing competitors. An exaggerated devotion to sports reassures them of their physical superiority and fitness.

Middle age brings to such men the implied threat that they now are faced with decline. Their own sons and younger men who represent the ascending generation are seen as a threat to everything that they have achieved. Decreasing physical vigor and impairment of potency are perceived as ominous signs. As a result of the aroused emotional conflicts, depressions, as well as a host of other functional complaints, make their appearance.

Case History

It has been noted that this general group of symptoms tends to occur in men who have often been considered successful in their lives. The following case is an example.

This patient is a white married salesman of 48. About six months before his admission to the psychiatric service, he began to complain of depression, tenseness, insomnia, crying spells, and poor appetite. He felt that he was not living up to the expectations of his employer and redoubled his efforts at his job. Even though he was having his best sales year, he felt that he was a detriment to his company. His firm had recently installed a much younger man as sales manager, and the patient felt very ill at ease whenever he had to have contact with the new man. The patient consulted an internist and was told that he had no organic disease, but that he was going through the change of life and was given testosterone. Hormonal therapy produced no change in the patient's symptoms and he was referred for psychiatric treatment. The patient showed moderately severe depressive symptoms which made hospitalization necessary.

Past history revealed that this man was the second of five siblings. His parents were unhappily married and quarrelled constantly. His father committed suicide when the patient was 3. As a child, the patient was apparently closer to his ineffective father. The mother had emotional problems. His older brother was the mother's favorite. The patient was always well liked in school, but was never interested in participating in sports and always avoided competition because he felt that people would dislike him if he surpassed them in any way.

He was married at 21 to a girl his own age. She was an aggressive, dominating type of person, although the patient has never seen anything other than perfection in her. The wife has worked since marriage. There have been no children because of the patients feeling about his own unhappy childhood.

The patient was able to gain insight into the nature of his resentment of the new company official and to express resentment about some of the company's new policies.

Discussion

The mother obviously controlled the relationships in this family. The patient was unable to obtain his mother's approval and may have, in part, resented his father's insignificant role at home. At the same time, he showed some attachment to the ineffective father, since he was unable to gain attention from his more powerful mother. But this attachment to the "weak" father did not give him sufficient emotional security. He feared being pushed into an impotent position by his older brother, who became the dominant male figure and the actual father substitute at home.

Because he was unsuccessful in his rivalry with this substitute father, he developed an unconscious antagonism against dominant male figures. Upon reaching middle age himself, his insecurities became reactivated. Having identified himself in part with the ineffective father, whom he to some extent resented, he feared being pushed out, just as his father was. His strong feelings of rivalry with his older brother had created fears in him that others would feel toward him as he had felt toward his brother.

He was unprepared in middle age for the role of such an older male figure. Severe insecurities developed because he was not able to establish a satisfactory relationship with younger men. His illness was precipitated by an unconscious equating of the younger man, who became his superior, as a revenging, symbolic son. This young sales manager assumed the role of the avenging symbolic son, even though the patient himself had purposefully declined to have children of his own.

RESULTANT CONFLICTS IN LATER LIFE

The man who has not worked out a satisfactory relationship with his father will have emotional vulnerable points during various important climaxes of life.

The original conflicts are established in childhood. During the adolescent period, the conflicts became reactivated, and the struggle between father and son may become intensified.

The choice of a marital partner is largely influenced by the relationship between the individual and his mother. An immature mother figure can intensify the existing tensions between father and son. If the mother cannot establish a suitable relationship with her husband and makes excessive demands on him, the father's insecurities become increased. As his prestige in the family falls, the son may become more dependent on the mother and submit to the mother's emotional demands. The mother, unsatisfied in her marital relationship, makes excessive demands on the son and looks upon him as someone who must fulfill her life ambitions. The son's need to succeed will become excessive in order to win the mother's approval. He will become very concerned about competition. Uncertain about meeting such excessive needs, he lays the basis for later anxieties.

At the birth of his children, the man's anxiety about his own and his children's future becomes more pronounced. He may rationalize his insecurities by his concern over his increased financial responsibilities and a presumed desire to provide for them adequately. However, the underlying concern seems to be an insecurity in the role as a father and not being able to accept such a role.

When the son reaches maturity, the middle-aged man becomes increasingly concerned about his son's feeling toward him. As previously pointed out, the underlying feelings of resentment and hostility against the father create fears that his own son will assume identical attitudes. Such concern is not only expressed when his son reaches maturity, but a symbolic son in the form of a younger assistant or younger co-worker can activate it.

In such cases, the middle-aged man will attempt to work out his insecurities in the form of various defense mechanisms:

1) *Excessive demands of young competitors.* The individual defends himself by attempting to keep the younger men under close control and to keep them from successful competition with him by making excessive demands. Very often, we hear such men express their feelings in the form of "life is hard" . . . "life isn't a bed of roses" . . . "I have to prepare my son adequately" . . . "I have to toughen him up for competition." Such demands on the younger generation are often seen in cultural patterns. Initiation ceremonies among primitive people, the initiation customs into medieval guilds, and today's fraternity organizations make similar demands on the young novice.

2) *An overprotective and oversolicitous attitude.* This attitude, as shown in our first case history, may represent an attempt to pacify the young rival, and, at the same time, to compensate for the underlying feelings of guilt.

3) *Glorification of youth patterns.* A fairly common form of defense is an attempt to glorify youth patterns. Here, the individual, by identifying himself with the competitive young person, proves himself a young man and denies losing his own youth. He may overemphasize physical achievements and prove his hardiness by feats beyond his age. Bergler, in *The Revolt of the Middle-Aged Man*,[3] discusses such cases in which men tried to prove themselves sexually. They had "a last fling," usually with much younger girls.

4) *Intense anxieties.* The anxieties become overwhelming, the individual is unable to cope with them, and the attempted defenses break down. Either fears or overt anxiety states develop, or the patient may somaticize his conflicts in the form of physical complaints. In other cases, the feeling of guilt associated with the unconscious conflict becomes introjected and turns against the patient himself. In this situation, symptoms of inadequacy and depression increase.

TREATMENT OF MIDDLE-AGE CONFLICT

The management of the problems of the middle-aged man must not be based upon symptomatic treatment, but upon recognition of the emotional causes. The attending physician should be able to offer emotional support to patients with mild symptoms. The therapist's understanding is necessary to help the patient to gain a better insight into the emotional aspects of his complaints. There must be sympathetic interest in the difficulties which the patient faces within himself, in his family, and in his job.

The doctor-patient relationship is the therapeutic tool through which the patient is able to regain his self-confidence and self-esteem. During treatment, the patient may attempt to test his relationship by asking for specific suggestions. By doing so, he wants to establish whether the therapist would place rather narrow limitations on his activities. It is important to avoid this trap, for the patient will look upon it as repeating an experience that has been so traumatic in the past. In such a case, he feels justified in looking upon the doctor as a restraining father-figure against whom the original problem was directed.

Very often, the middle-aged man requires extra attention to his dependency needs, and he must be helped to build up a gradual realization that he is becoming self-reliant. More severe cases will require intensive and dynamically oriented psychotherapy.

Another important factor in therapy is helping the patient to achieve a secure role within the family. There must be emphasis on an adequate family team, and, for this reason, the patient's wife may need to gain some understanding into his problems; social casework seems to be essential in such cases. The unconsciously determined choice of the martial partner led to the selection of a woman who has difficulties in her own feminine role. Even after the husband's difficulties have been corrected, the wife will continue to suffer from her own neurotic needs if she does not receive adequate help. In such cases, the wife herself will require psychotherapy.

Tranquilizing drugs may be indicated in cases of intense initial anxiety. Amphetamines, such as Dexedrine Sulphate, are of some symptomatic help in patients with depressive symptoms. However, we must realize that the tranquilizing drugs, when indicated, do not lead to a solution of the underlying conflict. Such medication will be only of symptomatic help. If they are needed at all, additional psychotherapy will be essential to clear the causative emotional conflicts.

Electric shock treatments have been used in cases of more severe depressions. In such cases, complications, in the nature of confusion states and emotional excitement, are more frequent than usual, and make it necessary to discontinue electric shock treatments.

Treatment with various hormones, particularly with testosterone, has been the cause of much controversy. The term "male climacteric" was originally intended to apply to a symptom complex produced by diminishing testicular function. This was a relatively rare condition, affecting only a small percentage of men who had reached old age. Some authors attributed the varied complaints of nervousness, depression, potency disturbances, poor concentration, and loss of interest and self-confidence to a gonadal dysfunction, if the symptoms occurred at middle age. But identical complaints are characteristic of any neurotic disturbance. An editorial in the *Journal of the American Medical Association,* after reviewing the question, points out that the true "male climacteric" is a rare condition and that the term should be limited to persons with objective disturbances and conclusive laboratory tests.[6] The article warns against the "promiscuous use of male hormone (as) unwarranted and . . . harmful."

REFERENCES

1. Billig, O., and R. Adams: Emotional problems of the middle-aged man. *Psychiat Quart, 28:* 442, 1954.
2. Billig, O.: The management of emotional reactions in the male involutional period. In *Management of Emotional Problems in Medical Practice.* S. Liebman, editor. Philadelphia, Lippincott, 1956.
3. Bergler, Edmund: *The Revolt of the Middle-Aged Man.* New York, Wyn, 1954.
4. Meerloo, J. A.: Transference and resistance in geriatric psychotherapy. *Psychoanalyt. Rev. 42:* 72, 1955.
5. Curtis, J. L.: A psychiatric study of 55 expectant fathers. *U.S. Armed Forces Med. J. 6:* 937, 1955.
6. Editorial: Is there a true male climacteric? *J.A.M.A. 155:* 1427, 1954.

THE THIRD SEX*

WILLIAM H. MASTERS, M.D., and JOHN W. BALLEW, M.D.

THE varied aspects of long-range, sex steroid replacement therapy in the aging are of particular interest to the investigative endocrinologist. The basic questions concern problems of project rationale, technics employed, results obtained, and future investigative procedures. A primary precept of any successful investigative effort is the clear delineation of basic theory.

The fundamental concept upon which our entire investigative effort has been based is the conviction that there is a third sex existent in our society today. This so-called "neutral gender" may be considered to encompass roughly all persons who have reached an average age of 60. Not only is the neutral gender making its presence felt with increasing demands on our society, but our every medical investigation is directed toward increasing the group concentration in the future.

If the existence of the third sex is acknowledged, the remainder of the "puberty to grave" project rationale is easily explained. The entire purpose of long-range sex steroid replacement is the attempt to develop happier, better adjusted, more useful members of the "neutral gender," while they live out their increasing life span. There is not the slightest evidence to suggest, nor has any claim been made that steroid replacement increases longevity by one single day. Adequate, well controlled, sex steroid replacement however, can provide significant physical and psychic stimulation in the "neutral gender" age groups.

KEY TO AGING

The humoral control of our physiologic processes is certainly one of the keys to aging. The entire process of growth, func-

---

* *Geriatrics*, 10:1-4, January 1955.

tion, and retrogression in physiologic aging is stimulated or controlled by the endocrine glands. In succession, the pituitary, adrenals, thyroid, pancreas, and gonads are responsible for individual phases of growth, development, and function of the various organ systems. We shall consider here the function potential of the entire humoral system during the degenerative aging of the human body, as both male and female components approach the neutral gender phase of life.

There is no significant reduction in function of the pituitary, adrenals, thyroid, or pancreas during aging. The gonads are alone in their obvious and well substantiated functional retrogression during the fifth and sixth decades of life. The neutral general age of 60 is approached by both men and women with an essentially intact humoral mechanism, if we discount the relatively ineffectual residual function of the gonads. In other words, we are essentially intact during our 60's, and perfectly capable of functioning from a humoral point of view, as efficiently as much younger persons, except that we are essentially castrates. Thus, we have the delineation of a third sex as we enter the last ten to twenty years of our expected life span.

Exhaustive investigation of the thyroid function of aging individuals, fundamentally by protein bound iodine studies, has established the fact that there is no essential or demonstrable evidence of retrogression of thyroid gland secretory potential with advancing years.[1] The adrenal glands of the individuals in the 60's appear to be perfectly capable of increased activity, should the demand arise, and no function disability of the adrenals can be demonstrated even in the ninth decade.[2,3]

In experiments dealing with the amylytic, lipolytic, and proteolytic pancreatic activity of aged persons, a 10 to 20 per cent reduction of effective secretory activity has been noted, but pancreatic function at the level described for the aged individual appears to be more than sufficient for much younger age groups.[4]

FAILURE IN GONAD FUNCTION

Urinary gonadotrophic determinations in aged individuals showed continued demonstrable pituitary activity in the form of follicle-stimulating hormone production.[5] There is, of course, a real reduction from the preovulatory and the postejaculatory peaks of the reproductive age, and from the high, immediate postmenopausal levels of both sexes. However, there is still a significantly demonstrable activity even in the 80's, which suggests great organ reserve, and that it is lack of external stimulation, rather than an inherent factor in the aging process, that causes failure in function.

Pincus and coworkers[6] describe significant measurable reduction in both ovarian and testicular function in the aging individual, and bisexual production of both androgen and estrogen during the declining years. Although they are not sure of the source of sex steroid production, they incline to assign this measurable production to adrenal activity. Thus most current investigative data supports the thesis of a "neutral gender," or essentially a castrate population whose gonadal function is either completely absent or is projected at clinically insignificant levels.

One point of interesting conjecture is why the gonads fail. The failure is certainly not one of lack of adequate humoral stimulation. Both gonadotrophic and thyrotrophic elements are present in above average quantities during the male and female climacterics. The essence of failure must be considered to be within the gonad itself. Although there is as yet no definite supportive evidence, the fundamental cause for the premature failure of this weak link in the endocrine chain appears to be an inherent lack of organ function reserve within the individual gonad.

Some suggestive evidence for this thesis is found during mature adult life. Both ovaries and testes are easily influenced into dysfunction during the reproductive years. The gonads are infinitely sensitive to the influence of the other elements of the endocrine system. In addition, any general body dysfunction may easily interfere with adequate ovarian or testicular hormone production. The relatively short-lived gonadal activity appears to represent the complete effort of the individual reproductive glands. Unfortunately, as gonadal reproductive activity fails, so does the gonadal sex steroid production. This is the Achilles heel of the entire humoral system. If only reproductive gonadal activity failed, and sex steroid production were maintained, there would be no slow transfer into the neutral gender, and replacement therapy would have no place in supportive efforts of later years.

SEX STEROID REPLACEMENT THERAPY

What then is the present approach to sex steroid replacement in the neutral gender? In essence it is an attempt to treat the individual members of the third sex from a bisexual point of view. Advantage is taken of the state of essential castration associated with the third sex. Both of the individual sex steroids are used in combination rather than individually. Through combined therapy, every effort is exerted to avoid the untoward effects occasioned by either hormone when given individually or in a so-called "unopposed" manner.

With the presently considered ratio of 20 to 1 (in milligrams) testosterone over estrogen, most of the criteria for combined therapy are met. If women are treated with this combination of therapy, there will be minimal or no breast tenderness. Vaginal bleeding will not occur despite years of therapy. Conversely, there will be no lowering of the vocal pitch nor will hirsutism become a problem. If men are treated with exactly the same drug concentration, there will be no breast development nor the protein wastage expected in unopposed estrogen replacement, nor will the frankly dangerous vasodilatory effect of unopposed testosterone replacement in the aged male be a significant clinical factor.

The advantage of treating the individual members of the "neutral gender" with a basic medication without regard to previous sex is obvious. The pharmaceutical houses can mass produce the material at a significant price saving for the individual treated. In addition, it is infinitely easier for the physician if the necessity for sex differentiation in steroid supportive therapy no longer applies. Obviously, mistakes of unopposed hormone influence and of undertreatment are more easily avoided if a basic standardization of therapy can be worked out.

The physical and psychologic regenerative results of long-range sex steroid replacement have been well established and results published previously.[7-12] It is not within the province of this paper to review these results. Suffice it to say that there is usually an amazing resurgence of physical strength and mental awareness in the treated individuals as opposed to the controls. Once a plateau of regenerative activity has been attained, continued steroid support will maintain this plateau indefinitely. Withdrawal of adequate supporting therapy will result in complete physical and mental involution within a six-month period.

TIMING OF THERAPY

High on the list of unresolved problems is the mute question of when to initiate replacement procedures. In other words, when does the basic differential of sex disappear in the aging male and female? Obviously this must be a completely individualized problem. When 60 is suggested as the typical age for the development of the "neutral gender," it is with full cognizance that there is great individual variation. Many women have reached the "neutral gender" at 50. On the other hand, many men are still essentially male at 60. As a general rule, the male climacteric comes five to ten years later and is usually more gradual than the female menopause. The dramatic cessation of ovarian function, frequently within a year's time, is not matched by the testis. Apparently there is a higher level of organ reserve in the testis than in the ovary. Since effective pituitary stimulation is essentially the same for both sexes, a higher essential function reserve must be presumed for the testis. Only in this way can we explain the slower rate of function involution for the male gonad.

The present approach to replacement therapy is to initiate sex steroid support whenever the recipient has reached his or her climacteric. Although this is more difficult to determine in the male than the female, the slipping male is becoming increasingly easy to demonstrate, as concentration is focused on psycho-somatic evaluation of the individual personality.

If there is essential value in the "puberty to grave" rationale of sex steroid support, therapy should be offered before senility is well established. Reclamation of the senile individual is a startling and stimulating experience. However, it is too bad to allow senility to gain an advance hold when retrogressive changes are easily avoided by earlier replacement therapy. It is almost impossible to overtreat an individual, as long as recommended dosage schedules are followed, and the basic 20-1 ratio maintained.

REFERENCES

1. Starr, Paul: A study of the effects of thyroid medication on pathology and longevity in aged human beings. 1954 meeting of the American Geriatric Society, San Francisco.
2. Gallagher, Thomas E.: Technical advances in steroid measurement. 1954 meeting of the American Geriatric Society, San Francisco.
3. Tyler, Frank: Adrenal cortical capacity and metabolism of hydrocortisone in elderly patients. 1954 meeting of the American Geriatric Society, San Francisco.
4. Meyer, J., and H. Necheles: The clinical significance of salivary, gastric and pancreatic secretion in the aged. *J.A.M.A. 115*: 2050-2054, 1940.
5. Masters, William H., and Dorothy T. Magallon. Unpublished data.
6. Pincus, Gregory, Louise P. Romanoff and James Carlo: The excretion of urinary steroids by men and women of various ages. *J. Geron. 10*: 113-132, 1954.
7. Masters, William H.: The rationale and technique of sex hormone replacement in the aged female, a preliminary result report. *S Dakota J. Med. Pharm.* 4: 296-300, 1951.
8. Masters, William H.: Long range sex steroid replacement — target organ regeneration. *J. Geron.* 8: 33-39, 1953.
9. Grody, Marvin, Elfred Lampe and William H. Masters; Estrogen-androgen substitution therapy in the aged female. *Obstet. Gynec. 2*: 36-45, 1953.

10. Masters, William H. and Marvin H. Grody: Estrogen-androgen substitution therapy in the aged female. *Obstet. Gynec. 2:* 139-147, 1953.
11. Caldwell, B. MC. D. and R. I. Watson: An evaluation of psychologic effects of sex hormone administration in aged women. *J. Geron. 7:* 228-244, 1952.
12. Caldwell, B. MC. D.: An evaluation of psychologic effects of sex hormone administration in aged women. II. Results of therapy after eighteen months. *J. Geron. 9:* 168-174, 1954.

MEN ARE WEAKER SEX*

MEN are really the weaker sex. They have more severe emotional illnesses, more physical illnesses leading to death, a higher alcoholism, delinquency and suicide rate.

These are the findings of Dr. George Lawton, New York psychologist who has specialized in the problems of the middle years and old age. Speaking at Cooper Union, he pointed out that it is much more difficult for men to age successfully than women.

Dr. Lawton stated that men both in the realm of employment and sexual performance face more dramatic crises indicative of aging. The dividing line between the first and last half of life in men and women is very much sharper for the male. He presented a list of rules of "What Every Man Should Know," stressing that a man as he got older had to exchange speed and quantity for strategy, skill and quality.

Many a tired businessman is tired because he is overworking to escape from close emotional relationships with his wife and members of his family, Dr. Lawton believes.

A modern woman needs even more than her home, a husband and children in order to give her a complete sense of purpose and intellectual stimulation. Dr. Lawton pointed out. He said that every woman, regardless of her financial situation, needed a part-time job, community activities, and some creative outlet. He also stressed the point that women in the middle-income bracket tended to do less work than they should and their husbands do more work. In such a case a wife, in order to help her husband enjoy life more and perhaps even live longer, should help share her husband's work load and share his economic and mental burdens.

* Science News Letter, December 31, 1949, p. 422.

Dr. Lawton's recommendation was that both men and women undergo regular examinations, both medical and psychological. The psychological examination for middle-aged men and women would have the following objectives:

1) To show executives and professional men how to slow down, to switch from a strenuous life to a slower but still as interesting, nourishing one.

2) To show inter-relationship between job attitude and philosophy of life on one hand — and sexual difficulties (impotence, etc.) on the other. In women, the relationship between career and difficulty in establishing an emotionally satisfying relationship with men.

3) To save marriages. Seventy-five per cent of marriages ending in divorce could be saved if *both* husbands and wives went to psychologists not later than 10th or 15th anniversary. Fifty per cent could be saved if one partner went. Lukewarm marriages could be improved.

4) Relationships with children would be far happier as the children grow older, happier for both child and parent.

5) To study aptitudes of men and women; see changes in vocational interests and abilities; suggest job changes for men. Women could build up life outside of husband and children. Might need a real job some day, whether for money or not.

6) Both men and women need psychological guidance for creative outlets, even if they pass muster as far as personal adjustments go.

IS THERE A MALE CLIMACTERIC?[*]

ELMER HESS, M.D., RUSSELL B. ROTH, M.D.,
and ANTHONY F. KAMINSKY, M.D.

A NY discussion of the male climacteric must begin with a definition of the term. The word climacteric derives from the Greek *klimakterikos,* meaning a peak or climax. In the female, the termination of the childbearing period is marked by objective evidence of a distinct change. Menstruation ceases and the curtain is rung down on the phase of fertility with its complicated endocrine cycle of ovulation and menstruation. For most women this change of life is indeed a climax of great importance.

THE END OF FERTILITY

It may well be that an extraordinary female will continue to bear children well beyond her normal span of productive years. Gould and Pyle contributed multiple references to birth in women over the age of 60 — several in the 70's, 80's, and 90's and one at the age of 108. The *Cincinnati Enquirer* in January 1863, reported that, "Dr. W. McCarthy was in attendance on a lady of 69 years on Thursday night last who gave birth to a fine boy. The father of the child is 74 years old and the mother and child are doing fine."

This of course is in the "believe it or not" category, well outside the usual range of experience. The normal woman passes through her climacteric with variable numbers of psychic and somatic symptoms and is thereafter infertile.

Clearly there is no such great divide in the lifetime of a male. Fertility, real or potential, commonly runs on into advanced years. It comes as no surprise to the urologist to find men in

[*] *Geriatrics, 10:* 170-173, April 1955.

their 60's and 70's fathering children. It is ordinary enough to find motile spermatozoa in large numbers in the secretions obtained from such patients after massage of the prostate and seminal vesicles. Since castration has been introduced as a helpful procedure in the management of carcinoma of the prostate, a large number of testes has become available for histologic study. In our last 10 cases in which the testicles were removed — not because of any intrinsic testicular disease but incidental to the treatment of carcinoma of the prostate — 8 showed evidence of active spermatogenesis. The average age of these men was 74.

Belanoshiken of Stockholm recently reported a study of 83 men between the ages of 60 and 92, of whom 66 per cent had motile sperm in secretions obtained from stripping the seminal vesicles.

In discussions of the subject, the matter of potentia is often given considerable attention. In the female climacteric, potentia is not a factor. Sexual desire, satisfactory intercourse, orgasm, and all of the accessory elements of sexual activity may be and normally are unaltered by completion of the female climacteric, and are often improved because there is no longer any danger of pregnancy.

DECREASE IN TESTICULAR ACTIVITY

An attempt to equate the problems of the postmenopausal female with those of the male with waning sexual power is inept indeed. We can only conclude that an unfortunate and misleading term has been coined, suggesting that in the ordinary course of events a man passes through a physiologic and a psychologic change comparable in some way to that of his feminine contemporary. Male aging appears to be otherwise. After 50, the average male shows a gradual decrease in gonadal activity as reflected in a declining level of 17-ketosteroids, with concomitant progressive testicular fibrosis and tubular atrophy. The psychologic accompaniments of this process are varied and complicated. W. Fagerstrom, a California urologist, has commented:

The years beyond 50 are critical years for many men, for it is at this age that various social phenomena and the stress and strain of our economy have their greatest impact. A man in the business world has usually at this age attained an executive position of reponsibility. Buffeted by the forces of a highly competitive industrial age, the demands on his nervous energy may be extreme. His children have reached college age and the added cost prods him to further productive effort. Wives' tongues often become more caustic at this age, disrupting the harmony of the household. Thus, unquestionably the middle-aged man often suffers a change of life but the symptoms usually arise from extraneous factors rather than a lack of androgens.

There is a group of male patients who show diminution in libido and potentia combined with such other factors as hot flashes, sweats, generalized weakness, lack of mental drive and energy, lessened powers of concentration, feeling of inferiority, and emotional instability. These are the patients to whom the term male climacteric is usually applied. Insofar as it is possible to sort out the primary physiological changes from the secondary psychosomatic factors, these cases would appear to be more accurately characterized as instances of androgen insufficiency.

There is little confusion as to what happens when other glands of internal secretion fail in output. The insufficient thyroid produces myxedema; the insufficient adrenal; Addison's disease; and the insufficient testis, a recognizable and a remedial condition. In consequence, we should like to answer the question posed in the title of this paper by saying that there is no such entity as a male climacteric, but there is a very real and troublesome disorder which can be termed testicular insufficiency.

Fortunately, it is uncommon and, unfortunately, there are serious pitfalls in the medical management of testicular insufficiency. It may be brought about by congenital deficiencies in the testes which prevent the achievement of normal androgen production and hence the insufficiency becomes manifest at puberty. It may arise from the factors of atrophy and degeneration which may accompany the aging process, either normally or prematurely. It may be caused by castration at any age after puberty.

From the purely endocrinologic standpoint, there are two therapeutic approaches. If there are testes present to stimulate, they may be encouraged to overcome their insufficiency by administration of gonadotropic hormones. This would seldom seem, however, to be a rewarding procedure. In practice it is better to compensate for the insufficiency by replacement therapy. The problem of treatment of testicular insufficiency would seem to be relatively simple. Given a patient with waning libido and potentia, flushes, sweats, weakness, loss of drive, and mild depression, we may make a tentative diagnosis. We may further support it by finding a decreased excretion of 17-ketosteroids in the urine. We may then give it the final therapeutic test by providing testosterone by injection, by pellet implantation, or by buccal absorption. The symptoms disappear and the problem seems solved.

DANGER IN ADMINISTRATION OF HORMONES

The trouble lies in the facts that androgen administration to men over 50 is a dangerous business, and that symptoms of testicular insufficiency are often closely mimicked by neurotic and psychoneurotic patients. Two recent upholders of the concept of the male climacteric, Goldzieher and Goldzieher, state that the only truly differential point is that there will be a prompt favorable response in the administration of testosterone in the one group and not in the other. It would appear that we are being advised to give androgens to a fairly large group of middle-aged males on a trial and error basis.

Let us consider a group of 100 average males over 50. Moore found that 18 per cent of men of this age had carcinoma of the prostate; Kahler reported 17.5 per cent; Rich, in routine autopsy specimens, showed 14 per cent; and Baron and Angrist found 15.8 per cent in similar random sections, but advanced the figure to 46 per cent in a series of 50 consecutive cases in which the prostate was studied in serial sections. It would therefore seem that at the time they consult us, from 15 to 20 among our 100 patients already have carcinomatous changes in their prostates.

It appears unlikely that even a most careful examiner can distinguish which prostate is carcinomatous. Kahler reported from the Mayo Clinic that, in 190 cases of prostatic carcinoma found on autopsy, only 37 per cent had been suspected clinically. Those of us who practice biopsy of suspicious nodules know that even the most educated finger is all too inaccurate. Many a time after we have taken out a prostate transurethrally, we have looked at the specimen, have felt it, have said this is carcinoma, only to have our judgment disproved by the microscope.

If we assume that some 20 per cent of our 100 patients probably have a symptomatic carcinoma of the prostate, we must consider what effect androgen administration may have upon them. Whereas there is no proof that androgens cause carcinoma, there is adequate clinical and experimental evidence to indicate that when a prostatic carcinoma is already present, administration of androgens is most likely to accelerate its growth and promote its spread. It is only fair to confess immediately that there are some conflicts in the available evidence. Under certain circumstances, some authors advocate the giving of androgens for the control of prostatic carcinoma in refractory cases. There has been some indirect laboratory evidence that at times the administration of androgens may be beneficial, but by and large we must adhere to three general statements of fact. The first is that the elimination of androgens by castration, by adrenalectomy, or by cortisone administration ordinarily has a restraining effect on carcinoma. Second, the giving of estrogens usually has a similar restraining effect. Third, the giving of androgens often appears to cause acceleration of the disease. For biostatistic evidence, a massive survey correlating androgen usage with the appearance of clinical carcinoma of the prostate would be necessary, similar to the current study of the relationship between smoking and lung cancer.

ANDROGEN-ESTROGEN THERAPY

There has been a recent enthusiasm for balanced androgen-estrogen therapy, as it is called, and this too has been proposed for the male climacteric, even as it has been proposed for a multitude of other vague complaints of the aging and chronically ill.

The average urologist, as well as the average general practitioner, is poorly qualified to evaluate the complex hormonal interrelationships that are thrust at him by the endocrinologist and the drug company detail men. If estrogens are good for prostatic carcinoma and androgens are bad for it, what happens when the two are given together? We do not know, but we are reminded of the statement by Scott of Johns Hopkins that, in studying the effect of estrogens and androgens on prostatic growth, he has been unable to counteract prostatic weight gain in castrate rats maintained on constant dosage of testosterone propionate with doses of either estradiol of stilbestrol, large, small, or in between.

We are, by inference and in default of definitive information, constrained to feel that we would be doing a major disservice to some 20 per cent of our 100 patients if we submitted them to a course of androgen therapy with or without counterbalance of estrogens. Feeling as we do about the subject, it is obvious that Hess, Roth, and Kamisky cannot present any extensive series of cases of this syndrome treated on a horomonal basis, and it is fallacious to base conclusions on a few scattered observations.

DETERMINATION OF TRUE GONADAL INSUFFICIENCY

You might properly inquire what we do recommend for our patients in this category? More often than not, a careful history will provide much information of value in determining not only diagnosis, but treatment. The complaint of decreasing libido and potentia applies only with certain limitations. More than one patient has admitted that his sexual appetite at home may be low and his performance perfunctory or wanting, but in the extramarital field, both may be surprisingly good. Such a discovery in a history will at once eliminate the thought of any necessity for a hormonal approach. The problem is one of human relations and the degree to which the physician will pursue therapy will depend upon his interest in acting as a combination psychiatrist and marriage counselor.

The history will often be rewarding on other grounds. If multiple associated complaints are elicited referring to digestion, bowels, vision, headache, and the like, it may provide additional evidence that one is not dealing with a specific glandular insufficiency. If, however, the history and examination indicate a true case of testicular insufficiency and if the complaint is severe enough to make therapy highly desirable, one may accept a calculated risk. Testosterone therapy may be tried and it should always be short and intensive. Testosterone may be given by buccal or sublingual absorption in doses of 50 mg. daily for perhaps a week, or it may be given intramuscularly by one large dose of 200 to 300 mg. of long-acting oily suspension.

The physician must discriminate carefully to discount psychic effects which might well have been accomplished had a placebo been used. In the really satisfactory response, a decision may be reached as to the need for continued therapy as opposed to the calculated risk of stimulating prostatic carcinoma. Patients so treated should surely be followed at regular intervals with careful rectal palpations of the prostate.

Until further evidence to the contrary is available, we believe that androgens alone or in combination with estrogens are contraindicated for use in the male over 50. In the face of definitive indications for androgen administration, it is reasonable to administer it with a proper recognition of the risk regarding carcinoma of the prostate and with regular follow-up examinations to detect the earliest sign of its presence. We do not regard the vague syndrome of the male climacteric an indication, nor do we feel that current promotional efforts recommending this therapy for an all-around stimulation of metabolic processes or as a nonspecific tonic for the aged patient can merit other than condemnation.

THE FRAGILE MALE*

JAMES O. BOND, M.D.

ALTHOUGH some of us may still persist in referring to women as the weaker sex, it is apparent that, at the present rate, the weak shall inherit the earth. According to our present statistical trends, it is truly a case of "the fragile male."

MORTALITY RATES

While total death rates have been declining steadily and comfortably over the past half century, rates for women have dropped at a progressively faster rate than have taken for men. This has been most marked in the white population where male death rates have declined 50 per cent since 1900, contrasted with a 65 per cent decrease for females, as shown in the accompanying figure. Thus, in the United States in 1955, although there were 1,382,000 more females in the population, there were actually 200,000 more male deaths.

This excess force of male mortality occurs in every age group, and has been steadily rising in each respective age group, although it is highest for the early and midadult ages of 15 through 24 and 45 through 64.[1] For all ages, the age-adjusted death rates in white males in 1953 were 56 per cent higher than those for females. This is to be contrasted with the year 1900 when they are only 10 per cent higher.

It was evident to actuarians of twenty years ago that this increasing difference in male and female mortality would eventually produce observable changes in the sex composition of the population. Today it is becoming increasingly evident to everyone. Beginning about 1945, women began to outnumber men in the total population for the first time in the nation's history. By

* Geriatrics, 12: 489-493, August 1957.

1950, the census year, this excess was accurately measured at 1 per cent. The statisticians of the Metropolitan Life Insurance Company predict that, if this trend continues, by 1975 there will be a 4 per cent excess of females in the total population. This excess will be even more noticeable in the older age groups where it is predicted that, by 1975, there will be 40 per cent more women than men.[2]

LIFE EXPECTANCY

While these statistics may seem cold and impersonal, the effect of this phenomenon on the expectation of life should have warm personal interest for each of us. In 1900, a boy baby born in the United States could look forward on the average to 46.3 years of life. A girl born that year could expect to live an average of two more years, or a total of 48.3 years. By 1954, largely because of the elimination of the deaths from infectious diseases in infancy and childhood, males could expect to live 66.8 years. However, a female child born in 1954 could expect to live 72.9 years, an expectancy of six more years than the male. The male in the United States is only now reaching the life expectancy that his fairer peer reached a decade earlier.

Dr. Spiegelman, a Metropolitan Life Insurance Company statistician, has shown that men around 50 years of age have a 74 per cent chance of attaining the age of 65. However, women of the same age have an 84 per cent chance of achieving this age. The pessimist will bemoan this favor the gods of chance have granted the ladies, but the optimist will look forward with pleasure to the prospects of relatively unlimited female companionship upon his retirement to Florida. At this point, I hope I have been reasonably successful in convincing you that the proper modern rendition of Shakespeare's oft quoted phrase should be "Frailty, thy name is man." And what makes our male so vulnerable?

CHANCES OF SURVIVING THROUGH A WORKING LIFETIME*
(United States, 1900-02, 1929-31, and 1949-51)

Age	White males			White females		
	1949-51	*1929-31*	*1900-02*	*1949-51*	*1929-31*	*1900-02*
	Chances per 1,000 of surviving from specified age to age 65					
20	668	596	514	796	665	555
30	680	618	551	803	688	593
40	697	650	604	816	718	645
50	742	713	685	847	770	718
	Chances per 1,000 of surviving from age 65 to age 75					
65	600	556	545	709	612	579
	Expectation of life in years					
20	49.5	46.0	42.2	54.6	48.5	43.8
40	31.2	29.2	27.7	35.6	31.5	29.2
65	12.8	11.8	11.5	15.0	12.8	12.2
75	7.8	7.0	6.8	8.9	7.6	7.3

*Reproduced from "Insuring the Older Ages," by Mortimer Spiegelman, Metropolitan Life Insurance Company.

THE REASONS FOR THE DISCREPANCY

It has been suggested that excessive male mortality is nothing new in nature, and may in fact be the rule rather than the exception. It has been observed to occur in many different species of animals, and it has been shown that, as far back as 1763, this observation was made in a human population. As further support for this argument, it is pointed out that nature provides for more male births. The ratio of male to female births in the United States is now approximately 106 to 100. However, there are also cogent arguments against this explanation. The primary one is based upon the fact that this ratio of male to female deaths has been steadily changing in the United States over the past fifty years. Unless one is prepared to advance the theory that the fundamental biology of the sexes has changed over this period, the hypothesis that this difference is due to biologic differences is rather tenuous.

It has been pointed out also that there are interstate, inter-cultural, and even international differences in these ratios of male to female deaths. Nineteen North American, European, and British Commonwealth nations were shown by Spiegelman to have ratios varying from 1.2 to 1.5. The United States has the highest ratio and the Scandinavian countries the lowest. The conclusion seems inescapable that someone or something, has been "tampering with the U.S. male," and it is of course unlikely that fundamental biologic changes would be so selective.

CAUSES OF DEATH

In a statistical search for clues, careful attention has been given to specific causes of death, as recorded in the routinely collected death-registration data. It has been found that, with only nine exceptions, all the 64 major causes of death listed in the 1955 data for the United States showed higher male rates. Two of these nine exceptions were cancer of the breast and the genetalia, diseases which are largely peculiar to women. Heart disease alone accounted for over one-half of the 200,000 excess male deaths. The rate for deaths from heart disease in the male was some 1.5 times higher than the female rate. Of the specific heart diseases, coronary artery disease accounted for 93,-000 of the 100,000 odd excess deaths in this category. Accidental deaths were the second major contributor and, in this group, the male rates were over twice as large as the female. Other specific causes, such as suicide and tuberculosis, have male rates three and four times as high as those for females.

The above comparisons were made from all age groups combined. For specific ages, accidents are the major cause of higher male mortality from the age of 1 through midadult life. After age 45, heart disease assumes the major role, with assists from accidents, suicide, and tuberculosis. At the ages over 65, cancer appears in the list of diseases having higher male mortality rates.

FACTORS RELATED TO SEX DIFFERENCES

The most notable change in causes of death over the past fifty years has been the elimination of deaths from infectious diseases in infancy and childhood. The tentative conclusion from this would seem to be that males fare less well than females when subjected to the risks of dying from accidents or chronic and degenerative diseases. Several explanations have been offered for this. Perhaps the most attractive is that which suggests men have adapted themselves less well to the stresses and tensions of modern life in an industrial society.[3,1] The marked increase in death rates among males for those diseases in which emotional stress is thought to play a causal role leads considerable strength to this theory. For men ages 45 to 54 it has been shown that the rates of cardiovascular-renal disease and ulcers have risen over 30 per cent in the past twenty years, while rates for females of the same ages for the same diseases have declined by about the same numerical percentage.[4]

It is postulated that perhaps women handle their emotional stresses with more social but less anatomic disturbances. For example, the wife may release her tensions through her tears, while her husband must act manly and choke his back into his coronary arteries. Virgil, the Latin poet, described women as "varium et mutabile," and it is possible that this characteristic of mutability is standing her in very good stead in our changing society.

It has also been observed that women take better care of themselves when ill, and are more willing to seek attention for their illnesses. Sickness surveys rather invariably show mirror images of the pattern of mortality statistics, with women having the higher rates of sickness reported. Once having sought medical attention, it is possible that women receive better care than men. There are specialists in female diseases, which do not have their counterpart for male diseases.[1] Many of the serious diseases of females, such as cancer of the breast, cervix, and uterus, and diabetes, are more easily detected and treated than typical male disorders, such as cancer of the stomach and intestines or cancer of the lung. It may even be ironic that the one cancer of males that has been most susceptible to treatment, cancer of the prostate, has been treated with female hormones.

Other explanations offered for the differences in the male and female death rates have been excessive cigarette smoking among men, the fumes and fury of mechanized travel, exposure to war and occupational hazards, and even the decreasing hazards of childbearing in women. Upon careful study, however, it is found that although these factors may account for some small segment of the problem, they do not begin to explain the total problem.

Further research presents an interesting and imperative challege. Fundamental to this research, however, should be an awareness on the part of men that their heavier musculature, which is their biologic badge of masculinity, is probably no longer an advantage in the competition for survival in a western industrialized nation. Indeed, it may even be a liability due to the psychologic role it forces men to play in a society which no longer accommodates that role. Once properly oriented, perhaps men can address themselves to a leisurely search for the causes of their unfavorable mortality ratings.

WHAT CAN BE DONE?

It is not necessary to await the results of this research before taking some very practical steps. Accidental deaths of males at all ages can be prevented, but particularly should attention be given to the boys and young men. Then too, those of us who have so far escaped an accidental demise should begin to search for ways to avoid or relieve some of the relentless pressures that drive us up the ladder and into the grave. We should see to it that these pressures are not being built into our sons. We can all promote the very manly cult of routine physical checkups.

Having been practical, now to end on a philosophic note. It would be amiss if you were to assume that my major motivation in this paper has been to frighten the males into action to prevent their untimely demise. This would, I believe, accentuate rather than alleviate the problem. I would rather like to be remembered for having called to your attention a problem that is essentially man's doing, and should, therefore, be his for undoing. I should like to induce a little more humble, relaxed, and objective attitude of men toward themselves, for it is here perhaps more than anywhere else that the key to the solution of this problem is to be found.

REFERENCES

1. Sowder, W. T.: Why is the sex difference in mortality increasing? *Pub. Health Rep. 69:* 860, 1954.
2. Sowder, W. T.: Problems associated with the increasing ratio of male over female mortality. *J. Amer. Geriat Soc. 4:* 956, 1956.
3. Sowder, W. T.: The fragile male. *J. Florida Med. Assoc. 38:* 553, 1952
4. Kaufman, G., and Woolsey, T. D.: Sex difference in the trend of mortality from certain chronic diseases. *Pub. Health Rep. 68:* 761-768, 1953.

THE MANY CAUSES OF MIGRAINE IN
MIDDLE-AGED AND ELDERLY WOMEN*

WALTER C. ALVAREZ, M.D.

MIGRAINE is a disease which, in the cases of well-
adjusted, happy, and fortunate persons, is practically over
and done with by the age of 30. When it persists into middle or
old age, or when, after going away in the person's youth, it
comes back in a severe form, the physician must ask himself,
"Why did it persist or come back; what is the extra cause or
causes?" Then he must spend much time with the patient, who
is more often a woman, learning all he can about the strains
in her life. He may have to look, also, for hypertension, cerebral
arteriosclerosis, or an inheritance of psychosis, or mild dysrhythmia in the electroencephalograms. A woman with a stormy
emotional life can be harassed by migraine all her days.

There are three main causes for migraine: 1) a hereditary
predisposition; 2) a sensitizing factor that cocks a trigger in the
body or brain, and sets it fine; and 3) a set of triggers, any one
of which can start an attack in a few minutes.

THE HEREDITARY PREDISPOSITION

Usually one can get a history of migraine or a migrainous
temperament in the patient's family. In 95 per cent of the hundreds of my women patients, I found social attractiveness, a
better-than-average intelligence, and a decided quickness of
thought and bodily movement. Three out of four of the women
had a small, trim feminine body with well-formed breasts. Knowing these attributes, a physician should suspect migraine the
minute an alert and attractive woman walks quickly into his
office. It is well that he do this, because so commonly, in giving

* Geriatrics, 14: 433-442, July 1959.

[157]

her history to an assistant, the woman fails to mention headaches. Then, his diagnosis is likely to be only "nervousness." But why the nervousness — often with hypersensitivity, or occasional nausea or dizziness, or prostrating brief spells of fatigue or depression? When the physician knows at a glance that the woman should be migrainous, he will go ahead and draw out the story of either typical migraine in her youth or an atypical migraine in middle or later life.

Rarely can one hope to find much of interest on *examining* a migrainous person. The cause is in the brain, and few conditions below the neck affect the syndrome. My impression is that migrainous women up to the ages of 60 or 70 are more than usually immune to physical disease. They can have hypertension, and this can make the migraine worse. The important thing to do with a woman who, in middle age, is still suffering much from migraine is to discuss her life problems with her. Only when the physician knows what these problems are is he likely to help her.

It is questionable whether a person can have migraine without the proper inheritance. In those cases in which one cannot learn of typical migraine in the family history, one can sometimes get the story of one relative with a typical temperament or one who had an occasional scotoma. Thousands of persons have migraine so mild or atypical that they never know what it is that bothers them. For instance: my mother had the temperament plus some days when she felt the need for staying in a darkened and quiet room. I and my two sons have only an occasional scotoma, and my brother has an occasional "let-down headache." Thousands of professional men with a tendency to migraine have an occasional scotoma and never a headache. Thousands of women inherited the typical body and temperament of migraine but apparently failed to get the gene needed to produce sick headaches or headaches of any kind.

The Many Women Who have Migraines Plus Mild Fatigue Headaches. Hundreds of times an assistant of mine, after listening to the long story of a woman's nervousness, dizzines, nausea, fatigue, and headaches has admitted to me that, although she might have migraine, the syndrome was too bizarre for him to express any opinion about it. Then all I had to do was to ask the woman if she had two types of headache, one a mild one relieved by aspirin, and another, a terrible one that no drug would help. When she said, "Yes," I would go ahead and draw out the two stories: one, that of migraine, and another, that of mild fatigue headaches.

THE SENSITIZING FACTORS

In many cases the best thing the physician can do is to find what the sensitizing factors of a woman's migraine are. If he can do this, and then get the woman to do something to relieve her strains, he can help her. If he can't help her to make her life easier, he is not likely to cut down on the frequency of her headaches. As yet, I know of no drug that will work this miracle.

The sensitizing factor sets a sort of trigger in the brain — sets it so fine that it keeps going off. Many a woman must learn to live and think more calmly, or she must get more rest and sleep, or she must learn to make decisions quickly. She must get her brain into a less irritable state. Then, perhaps, the trigger will not be going off so frequently. Sometimes, in the case of a businesswoman, a vacation and then the securing of an easier job will help most.

When an Epileptic Dysrhythmia seems to Account for Repeated Migraines. Whenever a woman keeps getting frequent severe migraines for which no immediate cause can be found and especially when there is a history of epilepsy or violent temper in the family, it is important to get electroencephalograms made because the woman may have a dysrhythmia. Then it is probable that the headaches are being triggered by an occasional one of the little storms that are occurring in the brain. In the absence of an epileptic inheritance, the EEG of a migrainous person is normal.[1]

Mental Overwork. Many middle-aged migrainous women get repeated headaches when they have been carrying too big a load of leadership in clubs and other organizations. They are so good at this type of work that they can easily get to doing too much of it. Men and women who write books or compose music can get into a highly migrainous state when they overdo, perhaps trying to meet some deadline. George M. Gould, in his *Biographical Clinics,* gathered hundreds of quotations from the letters and biographies of several eminent writers and musicians to show that when they were rushing to finish a piece of work they suffered terribly from nausea and headache and prostrating fatigue.[2]

Why Migraine, after a Long Intermission, Returns in Later Life. One can learn most of what one needs to know about migraine in the elderly from the story of the kindly old prelate who, in his youth, suffered greatly from migraine because of much overwork. When in his thirties life eased up, he lost his headaches and was free of them until the age of 60. Then, with the overwork that came from his elevation to a bishopric, he was again prostrated by severe headaches, which came several times a month.

When a woman of 50 gets back her old migraine, she may be having trouble with a wandering or drinking or inattentive or arteriosclerotic husband, or she may be having annoyance with an unpleasant daughter-in-law or son-in-law, or she may be having a hard menopause. Or, she may be struggling to control a mild psychosis which makes it hard for her to live at peace with herself or the people about her. She gets headaches when she wears herself out with the churning of painful or unhappy thoughts.

As I pointed out in a recent article,[3] when severe migraine returns to a person after the age of 50, the physician must suspect injury to the brain by hypertension or cerebral arteriosclerosis, perhaps with the coming of little strokes. Occasionally, migraines will return for no reason that either the patient or the physician can discern.

Anything that makes a person tired and tense and abnormally sensitive can bring on a siege of migrainous headaches. Many a woman gets headaches when worn down by years of marital unhappiness, or months spent in caring for an ailing child, or in nursing a mother dying of cancer. Repeated attacks may follow a spell of insomnia or a visit from one or more uncongenial and perhaps dreaded relatives.

Resentments and Antagonisms. Smouldering resentments sometimes seem to sensitize the exciting mechanism. Thus, a woman of 45, with repeated and severe migraines, admitted that often she got to feeling "all burned up" when she saw in the public print some mention, not necessarily unfavorably, of her minority group. As she said, she was much too touchy, with a chip on her shoulder, and she was constantly suffering because of it.

The wife of a politician said that her worst siege of headaches came when her husband was campaigning, and she was constantly being outraged by the attacks being made on him in the opposition newspapers.

Another woman who was having one severe migraine after another finally admitted that, although on the surface she seemed calm, she was always a seething furnace inside, full of hates and hurts and animosities and dislikes.

Worry. Worry and anxiety often sensitize the migraine-producing mechanism. Some patients say that worry is their worst enemy.

Internal Secretions. The fact that many a woman is free from sick headaches during a pregnancy suggests an effect from the internal secretions, but it is hard to say just what it is, because many migrainous women are well during one pregnancy and full of headache in another pregnancy. The sex of the fetus is not what determines the type of the reaction. Also, many a woman is freed from her migraine during only one-half of her pregnancy.

I have been surprised to find how seldom the migrainous women I see have their headaches with their periods. Some women get their headaches *before* the period, while others get it *during* or *after* it. A few get a headache with their *mittelschmerz*. Curiously, some women who had severe migraine in childhood say they lost it when they began to menstruate or later when they married.

Menstrual headache is thought by some to be caused by the accumulation of water in the tissues, and a few women say that they can avoid a menstrual storm by taking less salt and water just before the period or by then taking a diuretic. Certainly, some women who suffer from migraine at the period note that their rings are tight at that time.

Lack of Relief after Castration. That ovarian function in women is not essential to the continuation of severe migraine has been shown by the records of the last 113 women I have seen who, for their migraine, were given either a total hysterectomy or enough pelvic surgery to bring a menopause. *Not a single one* said she had lost her headaches. In a number of these cases, what with the flushes and the depression that followed the operation, the women was much more headachy, miserable, and unhappy than she was before. A number told me of a lifetime of suffering from migraine that followed castration in their twenties or thirties.

Migraine in Men. Curiously, in a very few migrainous men a headache occurs periodically once a month. I know a man of homosexual type who has such a severe headache every thirty days. Liveing reported a similar case in 1873.[4] Men with migraine can usually keep at work during an attack. Whenever I find a middle-aged man with a severe or prostrating migraine, I look for a second inheritance of psychosis or epilepsy, and often I find it.

To illustrate: as I write this, in comes a man of 47 who, every two or three days, is almost prostrate by a sick headache. He inherited severe migraine from both his father and his mother; but worse yet, he inherited from his paternal forbears enough of a tendency to psychosis to give him a stormy emotional life. His father, his father's father, and this grandfather's brothers were alcoholics. One of his father's sisters was so depressed she had to have shock treatments.

Chemical or Metabolic Tides in the Body can Stir up Migraine. Many migrainous persons get their attacks of migraine at a certain hour of the day or night. Thus, in an eight-year study, I found that 69 of 107 of my scintillating scotomas came between the hours of 10A.M. and 1 P.M. This suggests that the storm comes with some tide in the metabolism of the body or the brain. Reinforcing this idea is the fact that, for many years, I used to get a pseudo-ulcer type of hunger pain at this same time of day, when now I get most of my scotomas.

In some cases, the coming of an aura shows that, preceding a headache, something happens to the metabolism of the body or brain. The husband of a migranous woman may say, "I know when she is building up to an attack because, the evening before, she is usually talkative, energetic, euphoric, amorous, hungry, thirsty, or slightly manic. She may then have a bad breath, which is unusual for her."

Some of my patients said they got some warning of a coming headache as long as *three days before* — one developed a big appetite, another became very energetic, and another had three days of nausea and abdominal pain. One woman used to wake with a pale ring of skin around her mouth which told her relatives that she would have migraine that day.

Like many another migrainous woman, George Eliot at times used to say that she was feeling so "dangerously well" that she feared a headache was on its way. An able scientist tells me that whenever his wife is building up to a migraine she gets a bit edematous. Some women say that in an aura they urinate frequently, or they get very thirsty.

Curious Observations. Some women get their migraines only in winter. I often wonder why a nervous strain will produce in one woman a series of headaches, while in another woman it will produce a peptic ulcer, hypertension, mucous colics, repeated belchings, regurgitation, heartburn, excessive perspiration, frequent urination, or a neurodermatosis? Why, also, should the insane woman with her stormy emotions rarely suffer from migraine? Several superintendents of mental hospitals have told me that their patients rarely complain of migraine.

Boredom. Curiously, migraines can become acute when a woman is bored, perhaps without enough to do. A long-overworked widow began to suffer from migraine when her sons graduated from college and began to send her each month enough money so that she no longer had to work. I remember, also, a physician who, at the start of World War II, gave up a busy practice and was sent to Mayo's for a refresher course. There, with only a series of lectures to attend each day, he soon was having one severe migraine after another. He and I studied the problem with care, but could find no explanation for the bad flare-up in his formerly infrequent and mild type of migraine. Later, he wrote to say that he quit having the headaches the day a shipful of wounded men arrived in his previously almost empty hospital.

A Letup of Strain. Many persons get their migraines when they experience a letup of strain. Nurses get their migraine on their day off, some women get their attack the day after their maid's day off, and women who head church choirs get their migraine on Monday. Some men get their migraines Friday afternoons after paying off their employees.

Puzzling Cases. There are cases in which a highly migrainous woman will maintain that her life is easy, her husband is kind and loving, her children are good, and she cannot think of anything that could either sensitize her or serve as a trigger. In such a case, I say to the woman that if I could only live for a day as a guest in her home, or if for a day I could work alongside her in her office, I would probably see what the disturbing factors are.

Once, when I *did* drop in for a weekend visit at the home of a well-to-do woman who was having terrible attacks of migraine, without any trigger mechanism that she could recognize, I saw in a few minutes what the main causes were. I saw a very disturbing mother-in-law; also, a "difficult" son, much disliked by his father; also, a problem of much entertaining of out-of-town buyers; and much fatigue due to foolish efforts at making the house run "just-so." When the mother-in-law was given her own apartment, when the son was sent away to a boarding school, when the husband did his entertaining at his club, and the woman tried to be less fussy as a housekeeper, she became almost well.

TRIGGER INCIDENTS

There are many ways of tripping the trigger and throwing the patient into a sick headache. Following is an account of some of them.

Any Happening out of the Ordinary. In the cases of many women, one of the commonest triggers is some happening that is out of the ordinary routine. The migrainous woman too often tries to plan everything, and to set even a time limit when each job is to be finished. Then, if the work is not done perfectly and exactly on time, she may get upset, and, with this, a migrainous headache is likely to start.

Many women say, "I get a headache whenever anything goes wrong and I get flustered;" or "I cannot stand any confusion around me;" or "I cannot stand a crowd or much cross-talk at a tea."

Some elderly women will be thrown into a migraine by a surprise, even when it is pleasant — as when a loved son or daughter returns, unannounced, from college or from a trip. Some women can get migraine when embarrassed. Some get migraine whenever, at the place where they work, they have to change from the day shift to the night shift.

Sight-seeing, Shopping, and Fatigue. A very common trigger is the fatigue of sight-seeing or shopping. In the cases of many migrainous women, walking through a museum or store is likely soon to bring great fatigue, and then the woman must hurry home if she is to avoid getting a sick headache. Some migrainous women go into an attack after spending hours getting a "permanent."

Acute Tension. Getting tense can often bring a spell, as when a woman gets apprehensive over an appointment she has to meet, a plane she has to catch, or a job she has to finish. For instance, I have known migrainous bank tellers who got a headache about 2 P.M., when flustered over seeing a queue of persons waiting in front of their wicket.

Hurrying, or Being Hurried. Many women say that one of their worst enemies is hurry, or a feeling that they should be getting after some member of the family who apparently is going to be late to an appointment. Some women get a headache whenever they fear that a husband or son is going to leave the house late for work.

Too much Responsibility. Some women will get a migraine when they feel that too much responsibility is being put on them.

Anticipations. Migraine can result from anticipation of some happening, whether exciting, unpleasant, or even desired and pleasant. Thus, women have told me of going into a sick headache just from waiting for a loved husband or son to telephone or to arrive on a train. Anything that brings a feeling of suspense can start an attack.

Dread of Some Happening or Task. Some women get a series of headaches whenever they dread some happening, such as the visit of a domineering mother-in-law, or whenever they have to face some unpleasant task. I saw a woman who was having repeated vomiting spells, so severe that her physicians suspected intestinal obstruction. I soon learned that she, a poorly educated secretary brought up in a poor home, had married her boss, the city's leading lawyer and clubman. On their return from their honeymoon, the husband had said, "Now we must have a series of dinners." Unfortunately, with her lack of experience, the first party dragged terribly; after that, whenever her husband spoke of giving a dinner, she went into a spell of vomiting and abdominal pain, with a headache so mild that she failed to mention it.

Looking at Bright or Flickering Lights or Certain Designs. The migrainous woman often gets a sick headache when she is exposed to a strong light, perhaps on a beach, or reflected from a road, a glass desk top, shining organ pipes, a tessellated floor, or a number of mirrors. Soranus of Ephesus (125 A.D.) told of persons who get a scotoma if they look at a spinning potter's wheel, or at the glints of the sun on the surface of a lake![5]

Some migrainous women cannot stand sewing on a fabric with a striped or checked pattern; some cannot even iron a dress with such a pattern. Others quickly have to flee if they enter a room with a certain eye-twisting or eye-pulling type of wall paper. Some cannot go to a symphony concert because the sight of the violin bows going up and down soon brings a sick headache. Others cannot watch television, especially when, for an occasional few seconds, the image is replaced by moving or jumping lines. Many women are greatly distressed by a flickering light, such as that produced when their train runs past a hundred freight cars standing on a track on the sunny side.

Allergy. A few migrainous women can quickly bring on a headache by eating a food to which they are sensitive. Chocolate appears to be the commonest offender. One woman, highly sensitive to milk, was cured when I got her to make bread without milk. I know persons who can quickly bring on an attack by drinking ginger ale, or Coca-Cola, or coffee.

Some physicians used to claim that migraine is just a form of allergy, but I feel sure that allergy is only one of the many triggers that can trip the migrainous "trap." Many of the patients I see with migraine are careful to avoid the foods they must not eat, but still they have sick headaches triggered by other causes.

Curiously, in many cases the food allergen that gives a migrainous woman severe abdominal pain or painful canker sores is unable to give her a headache.

Overeating. A few women say that in their case overeating can bring a headache.

Drugs. Some persons report getting a headache on taking some drug, such as theobromine, aspirin, or a dye used in x-ray studies of the gallbladder. One woman told me she always went into a spell of migraine when her doctor gave her a shot of liver and iron.

Smells. Some persons can quickly get a sick headache when they smell something that offends them, such as a paint or a varnish or odors from a hot kitchen. A woman had to change beauty parlors because her hairdresser reeked of garlic! A migrainous woman rejoiced when given a job at a cosmetic counter, but soon she had to quit because of repeated sick headaches brought on by smelling some of the perfumes.

Frights and Fears. A sudden fright can bring a spell. For instance, a woman, when called to the telephone, heard that

Columbus, Ohio, was calling. Because her daughter lived there, she jumped to the conclusion that something terrible had happened to a grandchild, and a great fear struck at her heart. Before Central could explain that it was a business call for her husband, her head was throbbing with migraine. During World War II, many a woman with a son overseas went into an attack of migraine just from seeing a telegraph boy coming up the street; she was so fearful that the message was a tragic one for her.

One morning, as he left for work, a man asked his migrainous wife, "Did you remember to pay that installment on my life insurance?" For a minute she was terrified because she could not remember having written the check and, if she hadn't sent the money, it might be disastrous because her husband had been so seriously ill during the year that he might not have been able to reinstate a lapsed policy. The woman rushed to her desk and was greatly relieved to find the stub of the check, but a few minutes later she went into an attack of migraine so severe that she was ill for two days.

Anger. In some migrainous persons, anger can quickly bring a headache. Several women told me they always went into a spell when they lost their temper. A migrainous red-headed and hot-tempered woman was so angered at being left waiting at the church by the scamp who had promised to be there to marry her that she went into a spell of vomiting so violent and lasting that at four next morning a surgeon explored her abdomen. He found nothing, because what she had was an unusually violent attack of her old migraine. She had similar spells on other occasions when she got angry enough.

Noise. Some women will quickly get a headache if subjected to noises, as from a blaring radio or a jazz orchestra. A hundred migrainous women have complained to me that they could not stand much chattering or cross-talk about them, as at a tea or reception.

Certain whistling sounds, the scraping of chalk on a blackboard or a pencil on a slate, or the sound of a whisk broom on a bedspread, within a few minutes can drive a migrainous woman almost insane.

Excitement. Quite a few migrainous women will get a spell after seeing an animal run over in the street, or after witnessing any accident, or even after having a near escape from one.

Travel. Many migrainous women get an attack on starting on a vacation, or on starting back home from one, or on arriving home. Whenever a woman says she gets sick when she starts for home after a vacation, the physician may wonder if she is returning to some unhappy situation, but commonly the mere thought of a trip is upsetting enough. I remember one day seeing a frail and ultrasensitive woman go into an attack of migraine, just because she had to face being driven in her limousine from her apartment on Park Avenue to her home in Connecticut. Her maid had packed her bags and had dressed her, but still the thought of the trip was too much for her!

A Vasodilating Drug. A few migrainous persons, when they take a vasodilator, such as alcohol, nitroglycerin, histamine, or niacin, are likely to get a throbbing headache. I know a number of migrainous women who never dare take a drink because a few hours later their blood vessels apparently dilate, and this brings on a throbbing all over the body with, soon, a sick headache.

A few persons will wake in the morning with a migraine if, on retiring, they take a hot relaxing bath. This is hard to explain.

Energetic Exercise. A few persons can get a headache if they indulge in too violent exercise.

Sleeping Late. Sleeping late, as on a Sunday, will cause an occasional person to wake with a migraine. Some of my light-sensitive patients suspect that the explanation is that when they wake with the sun high in the heavens, the sudden blow of strong light on their eyes hurts them.

Sexual Intercourse. An occasional man or woman is thrown into a migrainous spell by sexual intercourse. The nervous system is probably so violently stimulated that the trigger in the brain is tripped.

Eyestrain. In my experience, eyestrain is only a rare cause of sick headaches. I cannot remember when a migrainous woman said that her headaches were brought on sometimes by much reading or fine sewing. Notwithstanding this, every woman with severe migraine should have her eyes well studied every few years. The ophthalmologist should, I think, be particularly careful to correct with prisms any imbalance in the pulls of the external ocular muscles. I suspect this because I "cured" two of my patients by having prisms added to their correction.

Bad Teeth and Sinuses. I can remember only a very few patients whose migraines were brought under control by the removal of abscessed or impacted teeth or by the cleaning out of infected antra. Recently, I saw a woman who had been in a sort of status migrainous for six weeks. She cleared up the day I got a dentist to extract two teeth with the pulp dead under a filling. In rare cases, such dead pulps can produce almost unbearable spasms of facial pain like those of tic douloureux. Diagnostic is the fact that the terrible jabs of pain come when warm food is put into the mouth. The warmth causes the dying pulp to expand and press on the nerve.

Constipation. In a rare case of migraine, constipation is an exciting factor.

A Late Breakfast. A few women go into a spell of migraine if they cannot quickly eat breakfast, and especially if they cannot quickly get their coffee.

An Upset Stomach. Some patients say that "an upset stomach" can usher in a headache, but usually I suspect that the upset stomach was *the result* and not *the cause* of the nervous storm. In some cases, it may be an aura.

Excessive Smoking. Some women tell me that heavy smoking can bring on an attack of migraine.

An Approaching Rainstorm. A few intelligent and trustworthy persons have assured me that one of their inciting causes of migraine is an approaching storm or any big change in the weather. In certain places in the world, as in Switzerland and Hawaii, there is a certain type of dry wind (the foehn, or the Kona) which sets some persons' nerves on edge, and thus brings on migraine.

Exposure to an Air-conditioned Room. An occasional hypersensitive migrainous woman will complain that she gets a headache on either going into or coming out of an air-conditioned room. Many a woman of this type fears she will get a headache if she goes into a close or stuffy room.

Arteriosclerosis and Little Strokes. Many persons past middle age, who are suffering from cerebral arteriosclerosis and perhaps little strokes, get unilateral headaches, some of which may be due to a flare-up of an old tendency to migraine and others to changes wrought in the brain by a poor circulation. The spells may be something like those rare convulsive attacks that afflict elderly persons with no sign of hereditary epilepsy.

Causes not yet Discernible. As I said before, many attacks come without discernible cause, when the person is happy and at peace, or even asleep.

REFERENCES

1. Gibbs, F., and E.: Personal communication.
2. Gould, G. M.: *Biographic Clinics 1-3.* Philadelphia, Blakiston, 1903, 1904, 1905.
3. Alvarez, W. C.: Aberrant types of migraine seen in later life. *Geriatrics 13*:647-652, 1958.
4. Liveing, E.: *On Megrim and Sick-Headache and Some Allied Disorders: A Contribution to the Pathology of Nerve-storms.* London; Churchill, 1873.
5. *Soranus of Ephesus,* translated by I. E. Drabkin. Chicago, University of Chicago Press, 1950.

SURGICAL RESTORATIVE ART FOR THE AGING FACE*

Notes on the Artistic Anatomy of Aging

ADOLPH M. BROWN, M.D.

THE desire to appear well and youthful is entirely reasonable and human; often this wish is stimulated by economic and psychologic necessity. People have valued youth and beauty as long as men can remember.

The plastic surgeon can advise elderly patients about the visual effect of old age and of what means can really be employed to delay the *appearance* of old age, and thus make life more useful and happier for old people in a younger society. Or to rephrase it, the plastic surgeon can advise older people about methods by which they can appear younger and thus be happier in a society which places a premium on youthful features.

In order to be able to make an aged face more youthful, one must know the anatomic and artistic difference between the face of the youthful individual and the face of the older person.

Surprisingly enough, not much about the artistic anatomy of the youthful and the aged face is recorded in the medical literature. But early in the Sixteenth Century, that versatile genius, Leonardo DaVinci, great artist and assiduous anatomist, walking the streets of Florence made sketches and anatomic studies of people of various ages. From Leonardo and that other great draftsman, Albrecht Dürer, we can approximate some rules of artistic anatomy which indicate to us what seem to be the rules of proportion of youthful and aged faces.

* *Journal of Gerontology*, 8: 173-184, April 1953.

Presented at the Second International Gerontological Congress and Fourth Annual Scientific Meeting of the Gerontological Society, Inc., September 9-14, 1951, St. Louis, Missouri.

[172]

The face of the young and beautiful individual can be divided into three areas of equal vertical space. These can be called the area of the forehead, of the nose, and of the mouth and chin.

The critical vertical dimension is the area of the lower third of the face. This area is from the bottom of the nose to the bottom of the chin.

In the youthful and beautiful face, these three areas are of *equal* vertical dimension. When they are equal, the face can be said to be youthful, in balance, and artistically appealing.

The etiology of facial senescence must be understood before surgical intervention is attempted. The facial contour is normally guaranteed fixedness and integrity by three broad rings of muscles. Two are the orbicularis oculi encircling the eyes. The third is the orbicularis oris, the thin band of muscle stretched around the mouth. All three muscle bands are held in balance with each other by their attachments with the other facial muscles.

The zygomatic major muscle which is attached to the lateral corner of the orbicularis oris loses length and mobility. As it becomes more fixed it causes characteristic folds near the mouth. The platysma muscle loses tone and becomes more fibrous and the skin below the chin may "double," if the person is fat, or becomes redundant, if the person is thin.

As age approaches a few teeth are lost. The remaining molars are ground down by mastication and well known dental phenomena occur. They lose some vertical dimension intrinsically. There is some absorption and diminution of the size of the mandible, and the anterior upper and lower incisor teeth tend to deviate their occlusal surfaces anteriorly. Thus, there is loss of vertical dimension of the lower third of the face.

With these anatomic changes the masseter muscle loses tone. The loss of muscle tonus as a factor in facial aging is apt to be belittled. The loss of vertical dimension plus the atrophy of the areolar connective tissue results in the accentuation of the nasolabial fold and the skin of the cheeks become pendulous.

The proportion of yellow elastic fibers in the skin varies widely, but as years advance the histologic picture of the connective tissue below the skin changes to show an increase of collagenous tissue and a change in physical properties and arrangement of the elastic fibers. There is also diminution of muscle volume of the facial musculature with age.

Thus, so far we have mentioned that as age advances, the skin becomes atrophic, as does its connective tissue attachment to the muscles below it, and the facial muscles themselves. The teeth wear down and lessen the vertical dimension of the lower third of the face. Bone absorption occurs in the mandible and other facial bones. The chin, therefore, is closer to the nose than in youth.

Further, as age advances, the elastic tissues of the nose also atrophy, and the nose slowly responds and elongates in vertical dimension. The chin goes up and the nasal tip goes down. The skin of the cheeks begins to hang in crepey wrinkles, bags, and folds, for it now no longer is as fully filled by its skull, teeth, and its other contents, as in youth.

Baggy eyelids also tend to give the face an atmosphere of advancing years and decrepitude. Overhanging upper lids are very seldom caused by anything other than redundancy of aging skin. Sometimes this redundancy is great enough to occlude vision.

Several plastic surgical methods can be used to ameliorate this aging effect: 1) the face lift; 2) shortening of the nose, 3) removal of bagginess of the eyelids.

THE FACE LIFT

One method, the face lift, excises the excess facial integument and re-applies the tightened skin of the cheeks to a higher and more youthful position upon its underlying muscles. There it is anchored, with the tell-tale sutures hidden behind the hairline and behind the ears. The amount of skin to be removed is best judged with the patient in an upright position. The skin of the cheeks is drawn backward and upward with the fingers, and the appropriate areas for excision are marked with a dye. If the skin is drawn too tightly, the nasolabial fold is entirely obliterated. This tautness lends a distorted appearance to the mouth.

The incisions are made inconspicuous by concealing them as much as possible in the hairline. The incisions of the angle of the ear are concealed by the overhanging ear lob.

Surgical Procedure

The patient's hair is shaved in the temporal area and behind the ears. A wide strip of sterile adhesive bandage is laid along the surgical area border so that the hair does not intrude into the surgical field. The face and adhesive strips are painted with a mercurous antiseptic solution.

The surgery is conducted with a 1 per cent novocaine with adrenalin anesthetic. The needle is inserted into the ear lobe, then follows the line of projected incision. From this line, the anesthetic is injected anteriorly toward the outer canthus and to the nasolabial fold, halfway to the chin, along the body of the mandible and along the sternocleidomastoid for several inches.

A triangular section of the ear lobule is excised. This is to accent the curvature of the ear lobe against the slight tension to which it will be opposed later. The incision is then carried upward along the anterior edge of the auricle and into the hair area and forward and upward into the temporal area. A posterior limb of the incision passes under and posterior to the ear, in the postauricular sulcus. It passes into the hairline above the level of the tragus.

The margins of the skin to be resected are grasped with forceps along the entire incision. Lahey, Allis, or Kocher forceps or towel clips may be used. I use a T shaped forceps, originally designed for spinal operations. The skin is undermined as extensively as the particular need indicates. Generally, the undermining is carried near to the outer canthus, the undermining radiating to the nasolabial fold and over the sternocleidomastoid muscle. The undermining operation is confined above the fascia.

By protecting the fascia, the temporal branches of the facial artery, nerve, and vein are uninjured. Further, the fixation or anchor sutures are more effective with an undisturbed fascia. The anchor sutures are placed as follows:

1. Canthus area toward temporal area.
2. Nasolabial area toward the auricle.
3. From along the body of the mandible toward the ear lobe.
4. From along the sternocleidomastoid area toward the post-auricular sulcus.

Once the fixation of the fascia is completed, the forceps are pulled upward and backward, drawing the skin over the ear until the face is smooth, but not artificially taut.

With the skin now repositioned, being literally *rotated* upward in the direction of the temporal area and backward toward the auricle, the resection may proceed. While the skin is held in its new position with the forceps, under tension, the excess skin is trimmed away with scissors. The excision is most wisely begun at the critical ear lobule area. It proceeds forward up toward the temporal area, then posteriorly along the postauricular sulcus.

After four or five lineal centimeters are excised, the suturing of the skin should commence, beginning at the lobule. As the first few centimeters are sutured anteriorly along the auricle, the excision is extended ahead of the skin sutures, preceding it as the suturing progresses. Skin closure may be with fine sutures, interrupted or mattress type. Either cotton, nylon, or steel may be used. All are satisfactory. The incisions are protected with a wrap-around pressure bandage, with the ears adequately padded.

The operation is not completed until one is sure that there is no bleeding. Hematomas are to be guarded against.

Needless to say, one should, at the time of a facial rejuvenation operation, inspect the teeth with a view to restoring the vertical dimension of the mouth with dentures or other dental prostheses plump enough to literally *refill* the mouth with teeth. This will help to iron out the vertical wrinkles about the lips.

Quite a perplexity to the patients contemplating facial rejuvenation by means of a face lift is how to "pass off" or explain their sudden facial youthfulness after surgery.

Many decide to change their coiffures and makeup before returning to their homes and occupations. Some develop suntans and change their spectacle frames. Some adopt sunglasses for a time. Most attempt to explain away their youthful and refreshed appearance to a pleasant vacation and rest in attempts to head off speculation as to whether the change was due to surgery.

The perplexities must be resolved by women who have facial surgical rejuvenation after the age of 45 years.

There is a growing group of women who do not wait for gross facial aging signs to appear. Many professional women, much before the public, seek only a partial face lift as soon as the first signs of wrinkling appear. Most of the time the surgery can then be limited to the temporal area, well behind the hairline, with no visible incision lines. The convalescent time is a week or two; thus the entire procedure can be accomplished during a short vacation; no explanation is necessary. It is practically a prophylactic procedure. Such individuals remain young and never need worry about radical facial changes. They seek minor face lifts every few years. Psychologically, they remain youthful, apparently inexplicably, while their friends around them age.

Often the upper lip shows up to poor advantage because the angle between the nose and upper lip is too acute. For youthfulness and harmony, the nose-lip angle should be, in women, slightly more obtuse than 90 degrees and, in men, slightly more acute than 90 degrees. Sometimes it is possible to ameliorate this optical effect by adding plumpness to the upper anterior dental prosthesis, if the patient has such a prosthesis.

SHORTENING OF THE NOSE

The plastic surgeon is often called upon to shorten the nose. One of the effects he seeks to achieve is to make the upper lip more visible, especially when the patient smiles. The elongated nose tends to cause the upper lip to seem shorter than it actually is. Plastic surgery can increase the vertical dimension of the upper lip by shortening the nose. It makes the upper lip easier to see.

Why is the large nose ugly, and why does its correction cause such remarkable improvement in the patient's appearance? Various factors of artistic anatomy are involved. Not knowing them, the operator will obtain only accidental or occasional good esthetic results for all varieties of hump nose. These factors are: 1) the artistic anatomy of the face; 2) the artistic anatomy of the nose, and 3) the laws of optics as applied to the artistic concept of the face.

Esthetically, the large nose has a specific optic effect on the appearance of the face. While the eyes of a normal face are about one eye-width apart, those of the patient with a hump nose always seem closer together than they actually are, as well as smaller and beadier. When a hump is removed from the nose, the eyes suddenly seem larger, wider apart, and more luminous. Conversely, the nasal hump catches highlights of overhead lighting, and the highlight between the eyes tends to make the eyes seem closer together, smaller, and beadier in appearance. Psychologically this gives the owner of the hump nose a crafty, cunning appearance. Another illusion that the hump nose generally creates is that of thinness of nose and face.

But what is important to consider, from the point of view of facial youthfulness, is the length of the nose. The long nose, especially with a long, overhanging tip, tends to increase the apparent length of the middle third of the face and creates an illusion of shortening of the vertical dimension of the lowest third of the face. It does this by its overhang, or concealment of the upper lip. As pointed out, we associate age with decrease of vertical dimension of the mouth area of the face. A simple experiment will illustrate this axiom. Simply remove the dentures from a person's mouth. The lips cave in and even with the jaws kept at a position of physiologic rest, the vertical dimension is shortened and the individual seems more aged at once. (Is this not why people of advancing years avoid being seen without their dentures?) Ask the individual with removed dentures to bite, and the face becomes a caricature, with the nose almost meeting the chin, emphatically illustrating this concept of the importance of avoiding nasal encroachment on the vertical dimension of the mouth area, if the appearance of old age is to be forestalled.

If the nose is long or has a hanging columella, the upper lip seems to be thinner and narrower in its vertical dimension. Most of this is shadow effect, but esthetically the lower border of the nose should meet the lip at an angle of 90 degrees or more. Practically every operation for hump nose requires that the nose be shortened in its vertical dimension anyway, because of the law of optics that the interrupted plane seems short and the uninterrupted plane long. The hump nose, even if it is long with the hump, will seem even longer if the hump is removed. The nose must be shortened, therefore, for two reasons: 1) correction of the actual length, and 2) correction for the apparent increase in length due to the removal of the hump.

To see the aging effect of the nose on the face as a whole, before and after correction, the face should be considered in its sagittal plane and divided diagrammatically into four horizontal areas of equal vertical dimensions. The uppermost area, that reaching from the ideal hair line to the top of the head, is generally not considered in great detail. The other three areas are important: 1) from the ideal hair line to the root of the nose; 2) from the root of the nose to the junction of the nose with the lip (top to bottom of nasal base), and 3) from the columella to the bottom of the chin.

As previously mentioned, the nose occupies exactly the middle third of the vertical dimension of the face and that generally it is in the same horizontal position as the ear; it occupies the same vertical space.

An X is drawn through the root of the nose, its outward branch running parallel to the forehead and its inward branch extending down through the chin line. The ideal nose does not extend anterior to this X, either at the tip or along the ridge. The X has an angle of 25 to 30 degrees in normal persons.

The normal nose does not extend below the line drawn through the nasobial angle. All of these factors are esthetically important.

The lowest third of the face should be equal in vertical space to each of the upper portions, as indicated in the diagram. The vertical dimension of the area of the upper lip is ideally one-third that of the entire lip and chin area. In other words, the lowest third of the face is further subdivided into vertical thirds, with the upper lip occupying exactly the uppermost third of this space.

The nose itself is divided horizontally into five areas. These are based on the anatomic structure. The five spaces are vertically equal, and the upper two spaces exactly include the nasal bones. The lower three spaces include the nasal cartilages. The support of the upper two-fifths of the nose is by the nasal bones, rigid and unyielding. The lower three-fifths of the nose is supported by the nasal cartilages and the septum. The septum is the main buttress for the fleshy part of the nose, and the cartilages of the nares are accessory struts.

It is necessary to overcorrect when shortening the nose, because the columellar cartilage is thin and weak and when sutured up to its new position tends to fall back slightly. Experience alone determines the amount of overcorrection necessary.

Surgical Procedure

The details of the various surgical procedures followed to correct hump noses are described in the literature. All noses are not corrected to the same pattern. Each nose is remolded to fit the owner's face with as great exactness as possible, and the over-correction necessary in areas containing soft parts, because of biologic limitations, are taken into account. It may be well to include here a few steps to follow to obtain a good cosmetic result. First, the patient is photographed. The profile is the most important view. On this photograph are noted the planes as illustrated in the diagrams. These show graphically the exact amount of deformity and serve as excellent records. Next a plaster negative impression is made of the face. From this, positive impressions in plaster may be made. The plaster model is also kept for the records.

When the hump is accompanied with widening, the removal of the hump is followed by complete separation of the stumps of the nasal bones from their maxillary sutures and repositioning of them so as to form a new pyramid with a narrower base. This operation requires a stabilizing splint to insure a cosmetically pleasing union. It is supplemented by anterior shaving of the ridge of the septal cartilage; usually the alae require narrowing.

It is also necessary to resect a triangular wedge of the septal cartilage at its columellar junction to shorten the nose, and it is necessary to reshape the alar and lateral nasal cartilages to make the nose itself intrinsically in proportion.

On the patient who has had a rhinoplastic operation, not only are the changes rhinoplastic in nature, but the whole face changes. The eyes seem larger, the upper lip shows to better advantage, and the face, on front view, seems less angular, more oval, and more youthful. The youthfulness can be attributed to the change in the apparent shortening of vertical dimension of the middle third of the face.

Psycho-somatic troubles are recognized entities today. The fact lift and other rejuvenation operations should no longer be regarded as the stepchildren of plastic surgery. These surgeon-created facial improvements may be called somato-psychic operations, for they do, by artistic somatic change, produce psychic change that is desirable.

HOW TO COPE WITH MIDDLE AGE*

IF YOU are between the ages of 40 and 60 and have a chronic feeling that things are closing in on you, you probably are right. People in their forties and fifties make up around 22½ per cent of the population, and this percentage is slowly decreasing. Yet these same middle-agers probably do at least two-thirds of the brain-racking, decisions-making, tax-paying, civic-improving, meeting-attending, office-holding and college-tuition-paying. And the burden appears to be growing.

Middle-agers are like Mexican burros. They carry an incredible load and receive a good many kicks to boot. They are expected to make the vital decisions that guide the biggest business enterprises, the churches, schools and other bulwarks of society. But it is constantly dinned into their ears that a man or woman over 40 can't get a job.

Middle-agers are lectured week after week by articles in newspapers and magazines warning them of dire consequences unless they take regular exercise, keep weight down and relax their tensions. At the same time, their phones are constantly ringing with demands that they head up fund-raising drives, run for the school board, be a director, join the father's club, be a Brownie mother, go to this meeting, speak at that banquet. Their leisure, too often, is merely a change of smoke-filled rooms.

Today it's expected that parents will send all their children to college. The cost already is several thousand dollars per year per student. And this burden descends on the middle-ager about the time that the personnel department of his company begins warning him to put money aside to supplement his retirement income. The time available is short enough and getting shorter

* *Changing Times*, July 1961, pp. 43-45.

as the age of compulsory retirement, which used to be 70 or 72, drops down toward 60.

Not only does a middle-aged couple have to worry about their own retirement, but they increasingly have to worry about their parents. That's because parents live longer, just as everyone else, the proof being the growing number of couples who live long enough to have their children join them in retirement.

And that's not all. The middle-ager, after struggling through 20 or 30 years of adult life, swinging at the curve balls fate has thrown him, and once in a while knocking a single or even a home run, finds that he is unable to pass his accumulated wisdom on to his children. In fact, they appear to believe that his brain is already worn smooth and useless like an old ballet dancer's knee joints and that if he has learned anything, it's completely out of date.

The middle-aged father is made to feel like the old Navajo Indian chief. Once he was revered by the young bucks of the tribe because he knew everything they ever hoped to know — the lore of the desert, hunting, tracking, the weather and phases of the moon. But now this wise and learned old chief is patronized even by children beause he doesn't understand the cause of the vapor trails that crisscross the Arizona sky.

Finally, middle age is the happy hunting ground of the patent medicine man. A middle-aged couple may wake up in the morning feeling fine. But a glance at the ads in the morning paper will change all that. They will discover that they have tired kidneys, middle-aged colon and sleepless nights. They are commanded to eat special food (which, incidentally, isn't cheap) and to take extra-powerful vitamins to bolster their supposedly failing powers. Chances are none of this is necessary, but gnawing doubts are easy to start.

YOU'RE BETTER THAN YOU THINK

If you are in your forties or fifties, all this pressure and propaganda may have you down. If so, here's a little different slant on the middle years.

Because of advances in medical knowledge and living conditions, a person of 60 today is as good as a person of 55 used to be. Furthermore, doctors increasingly talk of functional, as distinct from chronological, age. By functional they mean how you feel and how you handle yourself and your job. As an example, who needs more experience, balanced judgment, keenness and understanding than the judges of our courts? Yet for them there is no set retirement age.

Consider these examples of middle-age fitness and the reliance placed on it.

Up until a year ago an airplane pilot was allowed to fly commercial planes until he was 70 provided his arteries and vital organs were still okay. Now the cutoff age is 60, but Dr. Stanley R. Mohler, who made a study of pilot performance and aging, thinks the 60-year limitation may not be around forever. He feels that "the golden asset of experience, that common denominator of sound judgment, accrues with age, and should not ultimately be lost amongst a complexity of regulations." Dr. Mohler, incidentally, is Medical Officer of the Center for Aging Research of the National Institutes of Health, one of the few places studying the problems of the middle age.

Minnesota Mining and Manufacturing Co., is an outstanding growth company that spends 4 per cent of its sales on new research. Today 20 per cent of its sales are in products developed in the past five years. Six of its most widely known products did not exist until developed by its researchers. If this gives you the picture of an organization headed and run by aggressive youngsters just out of engineering school, glance at this list of corporate officers and their ages.

Chairman of the Board	74
Chairman, Exec. Committee	74
Vice Chairman, Exec. Committee	67
President	63
Exec. V.P., Graphic Products	56
Exec. V.P., Sales Administration	64
Exec. V.P., Tape & Gift Wrap Products	61

Group V.P., Abrasives, Adhesives, Chemicals	51
Group V.P., Electrical Products	51
V.P., Research	53
V.P., Purchasing	58
V.P., Personnel & Industrial Relations	49
V.P., New Product Development	60
V.P., Tape & Allied Products	54
V.P., International Division	45
V.P., Engineering & Staff Mfg.	57
V.P., Roofing Granules	56
V.P., Reinforced Plastics	54
General Counsel	69

The Kennedy administration in Washington was thought of as youthful, but if you accept the forties and fifties as the middle years, then the President and all but one of his cabinet (younger brother Robert) are middle-aged. The President seems youthful largely because his two predecessors took office after their sixtieth birthdays. Actually, of the 34 men who have held the office, 27 assumed it in their forties or fifties.

There is a great deal of misinformation around, too, about what is called change of life in middle age. Actually, it occurs only in women and should have no lasting effect on the conjugal relationship. Dr. Edmund Bergler in his book *The Revolt of the Middle-aged Man*, says, "On the basis of complete misconceptions, there is a widespread belief that woman's sex life ends with the menopause. Nothing is further from objective facts; nevertheless the misconception persists. . . . Nothing comparable to the ovary's functional death occurs in man. . . . The middle-age revolt in man erroneously called 'change of life' is a purely psychological phenomenon."

A WAY OF LIFE FOR THE MIDDLE YEARS

The truth is, all in all, the middle years should be the most rewarding ones. And they can be, according to doctors who have studied the process of aging, if people in the middle years will do two basic things.

First, they should learn to say no to many of the outside demands laid on them.

Second, they should take time to cultivate a way of living that will maintain their mental, physical and emotional health and lead them to a long, pleasant, worry-free retirement.

Easier said than done, perhaps. The man who has just been elected president of the Kiwanis Club and who is chairman of the house committee of the country club, an elder of the church and a director of the YMCA probably isn't going to want to change all at once and spend his evenings studying stars through a telescope. Nevertheless, that, in the long run, is what is meant. As one doctor puts it, "The man with the long string of affiliations following his name in *Who's Who* may shortly find his name in *Who Was Who.*"

Nor are the financial problems any easier to manage. The two-car family may not want to go back to one car and invest the difference for a cushion in later years. Yet that, too, might be indicated. As to this business of making financial plans 10 or 20 years ahead, the National Council on the Aging, an endowed foundation in New York City, has made a movie illustrating what happened to one man who retired without making such plans. The moral it conveys, in rather blunderbuss fashion, is this. If you plan to sell your house and move into an apartment when you retire, fine. But if you plan to keep your house to live in, better get out the pencil and paper well in advance and figure out how you are going to do it on your retirement income.

When it comes to good physical health, weight is important. Many a man or woman thinks he is getting "middle-aged" because he or she is carrying around ten or twenty extra pounds. It doesn't make sense to carry more weight at 45 than you did at 25. In fact, doctors say that your ideal weight for the rest of your life is your weight at 25.

In the case of exercise, it's getting a little every day that's important, rather than a big dose every two weeks. It doesn't have to be formidable. A brisk walk around the block after lunch would satisfy some doctors. Others have urged an exercise break instead of a coffee break. The main thing is to pick out some mode of exercise that's fairly palatable and feasible.

Instead of dreaming (and doing nothing) about punching the bag, riding a bicycle, rowing or playing squash racquets, settle for what's possible — maybe that walk around the block.

Children often are a problem because parents are too bitterly exacting. A certain amount of rebellion is the child's way of blasting off from the security of home into the orbit of his or her own destiny. Early training will set the eventual course; shouting arguments between teen- and middle-agers won't. There's an old law called "The Law of Minor Concessions," which says, Concede as much as possible without putting the main issue in danger.

At the other extreme, middle-agers sometimes have guilt feelings about their own parents. If their parents are alive, the tendency is to try to shelter them when perhaps the opposite would be best. Modern students of aging believe that it's best for older people to live independently of their children.

Above all, don't let your personal life get out of your control. There are many hands grasping for your time and attention. Of course, you want to contribute to good causes. But pick one, or perhaps two. Do this job well and be firm about excluding the others. Local fame is a fleeting thing, anyway. Can you remember who was governor of your state in 1943?

Ten or twenty years ago you were preparing for the role you play today. Today you are preparing for the role you will play ten or twenty years from now. You can't start fishing or collecting stamps or investing your savings in the stock market or appreciating art the day after you retire. It doesn't work. In order to do any of these things in the future, you should start doing them to some extent now.

If you let it, society will load you up with more than you can carry. A man's house used to be his castle. But in these modern times the telephone and automobile have opened the gates for the world to crowd in. Close the gates a little bit, in these middle years.

The seamen in the days of sail had a way of putting it: One hand for the ship and one for yourself.

YOU'RE YOUNGER THAN YOU THINK!*

RAY GILES

WHEN classes in adult education began in an Eastern city, those who joined were asked why they did so. A 43-year-old man replied, "Because I don't want to die at 50 and have to wait until I'm 70 or 80 to be buried." He didn't realize it, but he was sounding what ought to be the battle cry of every adult in America.

It is only a dozen years or so since the modern, scientific study of aging, called gerontology, began to hit its stride. But out of the mass of provocative findings that have been gathered, one stands out like the well-advertised sore thumb. It is this: *Not 1 person in 10 gets the pleasure or achievement out of living after 50 that might easily be had with a little planning and effort.* Echoing the opinion of physicians, psychologists, and other specialists in this field, Dr. Martin Gumpert states flatly, "Middle age, the so-called period of maturity, ruins, as it is lived, today, the so-called period of decline."

What does he mean? For one thing, we get in ruts. We become too exclusively concerned with making a living or running a home. We give plenty of thought to financial security but little to building up mental and spiritual assets for the later years. We lose interest in one thing after another. We stifle our precious curiosity and stop learning. This makes life narrow down at the very time when horizons should be widening. Relatively speaking, we are dead at 50, but don't know it.

The average man at 50 is at the peak of his earning power and wants to keep it that way. Fear of making mistakes and "losing face" can make him overconservative. Too often he decides to "let well enough alone," just "keep his fences mended."

---

* *Better Homes and Gardens*, 32: 52-53, Jan. 1954.

This makes him a drifter who no longer goes ahead. His wife, around 50, sees her children marry and move, perhaps, a thousand miles away. This experience and the menopause can make her feel "all washed up" and at the end of the road.

The modern program for better living after 50 begins with realizing how much better off we are than our parents were. We have not only more years to live, but better health than they had after 50. Even more exciting are the opportunities all around us to make far more of our unused capacities for lifelong enjoyment and progress than any previous generation has known.

YOU'RE 15 YEARS YOUNGER

"You cannot begin too early!" is the slogan for this program. Studies of happy, go-ahead older people prove conclusively that they didn't suddenly become interested in people, places, current events, new developments, study courses, and their hobbies at 40, 60, or 70. While still in their 20's and 30's they made interest and participation in all phases of living a settled habit. So fortified, any man or woman can come to the eightieth birthday as did the elder Oliver Wendell Holmes, who exulted, "I had much to learn, and at 80 I find new vistas opening all around me!"

The daily practice of abundant living, as you see, has double pay-off. It can double the pleasures of existence at 30 at the same time as it paves the surest-possible road to happiness after 50. In a very real sense you begin now to enjoy tomorrow.

Life expectancy at birth, only 49 years in 1900, is about 20 years more today, and continues to increase. But note that qualification, "at birth." The older you become, the greater your personal life span is likely to be. Now that social security, pensions, and private insurance give most of us assured old-age income, it is interesting to learn what a group of life insurance actuaries found when they studied 1,000 male annuitants all aged 65. The conclusion was that 500 would live to age 80, and 100 beyond 90. For women, life expectancy is even greater.

Too many of us believe that we will die at about the same

age as our parents did. It still is an asset to have long-lived ancestors, but now the chances are that any person who has them will live to be even older. And if your parents died before they were 60, you should ask yourself, "Died of what?" Suppose your father died of tuberculosis or pneumonia and your mother of diabetes or influenza. These and many other diseases are no longer as fatal as they were.

Looking to parents as models for our future can create another obstacle to making our late years better than theirs were. We remember how old they seemed at 50 or 70 and assume it will be the same for us. But the same environment which gives us longer lives also gives us higher energy, keener minds, and better resistance to diseases. Doctor Gumpert says that a typical man of 65 today is as good "biologically" as was the average man of 50 in 1900. In effect, he's 15 years younger!

AFTER 50, YOU GET A BREAK

How young is "young"? How old is "old"? In your 30's you consider yourself still youthful. Actually, a lot of aging has already taken place in your body. Even before you were born, senile changes had occurred in certain blood vessels. You "aged" rapidly when you were a child. Your metabolism slowed substantially during the period between infancy and your twentieth birthday. Chances are, at 20 your hearing was less acute than it formerly was, and your knees less supple. You had become less able to indulge in spurts of explosive energy or any long stretches of high effort. By the time you were 30, your arteries may already have begun to harden.

At 50 you may feel that it is now too late to be changed for the better. Wrong again! At almost any age, simple disregard of the rules of good living may be corrected to your advantage. Suppose at 65 you're overweight. Even at that late date, you can improve your personal life span by reducing. But if overweight is your problem, why postpone reduction? Why not, at 35 or 40, begin now to enjoy the better health and greater energy that accompany normal weight?

Between the ages of 40 and 60, the most critical period of

aging occurs, warns Dr. Edward I. Stieglitz, another leader in geriatrics. "It is in this period," he observes, "that the changes which will ultimately disable begin and that we can hope to accomplish something by preventive measures." So, the worst of all mistakes can be neglecting your periodical health examinations, which may disclose trouble while it can still be nipped in the bud.

Between the ages of 30 and 40, a thorough health examination every two years may be often enough; but after 50, such an audit should be had every year. Its importance may be gauged by the fact that out of 10,000 businessmen who were examined, it was possible to tell 8,870 of them how they might enjoy even better health. Many degenerative diseases give no early warning — like pain or changed health — at all. As you grow older, your sense of pain diminishes. This is, at best, only a mixed blessing, because it can make you feel all right when something is going on which is entirely wrong. Only a competent medical examination can tell you accurately about the state of your health.

In his book *The Second Forty Years,* Doctor Stieglitz reports cheerfully: "Aging slows down as you grow older. This is one of the compensations for later years." At 50, most of your worst aging is already behind you. That may be why older people often tell you they don't feel much older at 70 than they did 10 or 15 years earlier in life.

YOUR MIND IS BETTER THAN EVER

This is not to pretend that at 50 or 70 you will have the zip and go you enjoyed at 30 and 40. You won't. But do not make the mistake of believing that as physical energy lessens, your mind must slow down correspondingly. It shouldn't, unless you beg it to. Surveys show older people giving up too many of their hobbies, interests, and other mentally stimulating and mentally demanding pastimes. This senseless renunciation only speeds the aging process. It ends up with "doing too many things for the last time and too few things for the first time," to quote the pungent definition of old age supplied by Doctor Gumpert.

After 50, we need to strike out for mental adventure, and with confidence. An interest in the stars, an itch to paint, or the desire to acquire a brand-new skill for full- or part-time employment after retirement should be cherished and indulged to the full. By taking action, we disprove the ancient saying "You can't teach an old dog new tricks."

In this effort we are encouraged by those who are studying the mental capacity of older people. In his book *The Years after Fifty,* Dr. Wingate M. Johnson declares, "The mind should be at its very best when one is 40 and should continue to be a first-class thinking machine until the proverbial threescore years and 10." Dr. Howard W. Haggard says, "The faculties of the mind may stay young, keen, and clear even into the 90's."

Authorities agree that any slowing down of the mind is very gradual; some say, "almost imperceptible." The ability to learn, to concentrate, and to be creative should exist into advanced old age, though you may need more frequent rest periods. Some mental faculties actually improve with age — like the ability to arrive at sound judgments. This is because increased life experience gives both depth and thoroughness to thinking.

YOU'LL OUTNUMBER THE COLLEGE KIDS

The boom in adult education proves our ability to grow mentally after 50, as more and more grandparents go back to school. *There are now more students in adult-education groups than in all our colleges and universities — and more older men and women taking correspondence courses and attending trade schools.* Roughly, they sort into four groups.

Group 1 wants to earn more money. Teachers, mechanics, businessmen, and others take courses which will make them more valuable in their work. Group 2 wants new skills in homemaking. Women learn tailoring, home decoration, fancy cooking; men learn cabinetmaking, plumbing, shopwork, home repairs.

Group 3 goes in for cultural enjoyments like sculpturing, painting, or weaving; or learning to appreciate art, music, literature, and philosophy. Some play in orchestras, sing, act, dance.

Group 4 does exactly what the experts urge older folks to do — they are preparing, definitely and intelligently, for better living after 50. Just as they studied books and took courses earlier in life to make good in their work, then planned and studied to be successful as marriage partners and as parents, so they now plan and get set for continued growth and enjoyment after 50. Like the ancient Greek, Aeschylus, they discover that "To learn what is new is to remain every young!"

Doctor Haggard says that even very old people should study difficult new subjects like law and foreign languages for mental stimulation and continued growth. There's nothing theoretical about that! Striking proof of the teachability of older people is contained in the 1952 report of the New York State Joint Legislative Committee on Problems of the Aging. Here Dr. Irving Lorge of Teachers College, Columbia University, tells how readily difficult subjects may be mastered by older men and women who resolutely kick aside that "old-dogs-can't-learn" complex.

In teaching a difficult foreign language, Doctor Lorge found no perceptible difference between the learning capacity of older students and young ones. It was the same with stenography.

The chairman of the committee, State Senator Thomas C. Desmond, made a survey among 75 trade and correspondence schools. "It proves," he reports, "that even the elderly can learn self-supporting skills when courses are carefully chosen." A weaving school reports graduates up to age 70 setting up in business. Men and women well past 50 have become successful in hotel work. Grandmothers take beauty courses and open shop. A law school reports two male graduates, one 75, the other 96, who passed their bar examinations with flying colors and are now successfully practicing law.

Well, what does it all add up to? Here we have a pattern of lifelong activity, growth, and satisfaction. Unlike older people in 1900, these men and women of today have no time or opportunity to "feel useless," "on the shelf," or otherwise trapped on a dead-end street from which there is no escape or return. They will go right on living well for years to come.

WHICH ARE YOUR BEST YEARS?*

JOHN E. GIBSON

AT WHAT age are you the smartest? When are you most likely to fall in love? At what age are you apt to make the most money?

To find out the answer to these and many similar questions, scientists in leading universities and research foundations have conducted exhaustive studies and surveys. Let us take a look at their most recent findings.

Q: At what age do you have the greatest physical strength?

A: You can expect your muscles to develop their greatest horsepower between 20 and 25. It is then that your biceps are likely to be the brawniest, your sinews capable of exerting the greatest force. A consensus of leading university studies shows that your physical strength increases steadily with each passing year until you reach your early middle 20's. But after the age of 25, your muscular powers diminish — so gradually at first that you are scarcely aware of being less strong than you were. But as age increases, your strength declines at an increasingly rapid rate.

Q: At what age is it easiest for you to learn?

A: You can learn almost anything more quickly and easily during your middle 20's than at any other time in life. Studies conducted at Columbia University showed that a person's ability to learn increases from early childhood up to the age of 25. After that time, it was found that a man's ability to absorb knowledge begins to diminish at the rate of about one per cent a year.

The late Prof. Edward L. Thorndike, in reviewing the findings of the study, pointed out that contrary to popular notion,

---

* Reprinted from *This Week*, (July 25, '51), 420 Lexington Ave., New York 17, N.Y. Copyright 1951 by the United Newspapers Magazine Corp.

childhood is not the best age for learning. For example, any age between 20 and 45 was found better for learning than the early teens.

After 60, the ability to learn new things is appreciably lessened. Thorndike found that a man of 65 can learn only about half as much per hour as he could when he was 25.

Q: At what age do you have the greatest mental ability?

A: Our ability to learn — to absorb new knowledge — begins to diminish gradually as we leave our 20's behind us. But our ability to *think* and *reason* continues increasing with age — provided these faculties are given sufficient exercise.

Studies conducted at several universities show that the *average* person's mental abilities decrease with age, but that this is largely due to the fact that most people let their brains get "rusty" after they get out of school.

At the University of Minnesota, investigators made a study of 5,500 extension-course students, whose ages ranged from 20 to 70, and who were engaged in occupations which made continuous demands on their intelligence. In the vast majority of cases, mental ability definitely increased with age. The average man of 40 had appreciably "more on the ball" than the person of 30; the person in his 50's scored higher than the one of 45, and so on.

Q: At what age does your personality undergo the greatest change?

A: Between 25 and 35. Studies show that in this 10-year period our tastes, interests and attitudes change more radically than at any other period in our lives.

And the consensus is that the older person possesses a definite set of tendencies which become more pronounced with each passing year:

1) He becomes more and more introverted, more given to self-examination, with a tendency to prefer his own company to that of others. (These traits have been found to be more pronounced in women than in men.)

2) His interest in most former amusements (dancing, movies, sports, etc.) shows a marked decline. His interest in cultural

activities (concerts, lectures, art galleries) increases.

3) He gets more and more enjoyment out of reading. But his interest in fiction decreases. He prefers magazine articles and newspapers.

4) His interest in politics and religion steadily increases with each passing year.

Q: At what age are you most emotional?

A: At Brown University, Prof. William Royce Willoughby analyzed the personalities of nearly 1,400 persons of both sexes, ages 15 to 75. He found that women were the most emotional between 55 and 60; that their second highest peak was reached at about their 30th birthday; that they were calmest and least emotional between 45 and 50.

The study showed women to be much more emotional than men at all age levels. The men showed little change in emotionality with age — except for a comparatively slight upsurge in the 40's, and again in the 50's.

Q: At what age are you likely to do your most creative work?

A:. The most comprehensive survey on this question has been made by Harvey C. Lehman, professor of psychology at Ohio University. He made a detailed analysis of the years of greatest productivity in various professions, arts and sciences. Here are the findings of his study, which took 20 years to complete:

The age of greatest proficiency in science, mathematics and practical invention is 33 to 44. The most productive years for physicians and medical researchers were found to be between 35 and 39. The peak years for psychologists were likewise found to be from 35 to 39.

Most painters and composers do their best work before the age of 35. And explorers make their most notable discoveries in their early 30's. Poets generally produce their best work between 26 and 30. Short-story writers turn out most work between ages 22 and 37. Novelists are most successful in hitting the literary jackpot between 40 and 44.

Q: At what age are you likely to earn the most money?

A: Though your most creative years are likely to be the 30's, the odds are far better than even that during your middle 50's you'll earn more money than at any other period in your life.

Wide-scale studies of the earning power of various age groups, conducted at Ohio University, have shown that under current conditions a man's earned income is likely to be the greatest at about 55 or 56.

And a further survey made at the same university has shown that the ages of most of the nation's top-flight executives range between 55 and 60. So if you haven't made your "pile" by the time you're 40, don't let it discourage you. The "golden fifties" are the jackpot decade.

Q: At what age are you most apt to fall in love?

A: If you're a woman, studies show that you're likely to be most susceptible during your late teens, with 18 being the most vulnerable year. Men are most likely to be smitten between 20 and 25. After these peak periods are past, susceptibility of both sexes tends to wane until they reach their 40's. Then it takes a sudden upswing — particularly among women.

Q: At what age is a woman the most beautiful?

A: The National Institute of Public Opinion conducted a nationwide survey in which men and women of every age and walk of life were asked to vote on this question. Most people considered that a woman reaches the peak of her beauty in her early 20's.

Less than one person in five considered the late teens the most beautiful age. Indeed, the bloom of youth and innocence as typified by the 18-year-old was esteemed even less by voters in the upper-age brackets. And only about one in eight subscribed to the view that a lady is more fascinating when she reaches 30.

Q: At what age are you most sensitive to pain?

A: If you hit your thumb with a hammer when you're 40, it won't hurt nearly as much as it would have if you had been only 20. The noted psychiatrist William P. Chapman tested the pain reactions of 200 persons, ranging in age from 10 to 85 years. He found that for the overwhelming majority, sensitivity to pain decreases progressively with age. His study showed that a young man of 20 is, on the average, 22 per cent more sensitive to pain than a person of over 45. Moral: avoid getting hurt when you're young — it feels worse then.

Q: At what age are people most irritable and hardest to get along with?

A: To find out the answer to this question, psychologist Hulsey Cason of the University of Wisconsin made a study of over a thousand subjects, age 10 to 90. He found that middle-aged people (40 to 60) were more easily annoyed than any other age group. Young people were the least irritable, but each year that brought them closer to middle age found them more easily upset by trifles, and more inclined to be peevish and impatient.

But after middle age is passed, the psychologist found that people's dispositions tend to become more serene.

Q: At what age are your reactions the quickest?

A: University studies show that your physical reactions speed up with each passing year — until you reach your middle 20's, then slow up. By the time you are 60 you respond to things with just about half the speed that you did when you were 25. In other words, it takes twice as long for your brain to transmit an impulse and your body to act on it.

That's one reason why oldsters are more subject to accidents. They see danger coming, but their physical reaction to it is frequently several seconds outside the safety margin.

A young man hears an auto's horn and is out of the way almost at the same time the driver's hand touches the button. An older man hears the horn at the same time — but his reflexes are less instantaneous.

❋   ❋   ❋

Picking the best years of your life is not easy. The advantages and disadvantages of each age tend to almost offset each other.

Some of our faculties and abilities function better as we grow older; with others the opposite is true. Science can put the attributes of each age under the clinical microscope, but it takes a Solomon to add up the debits and credits and decide which of the years of your life are the best.

LET GO OF THE DREAM*

MANY middle-aged men and women feel like failures when they aren't failures at all. They are merely using the wrong tape measure. They look at themselves in their 40's and 50's and take their measures by the standards of childhood dreams and ambitions.

These standards are as ill-fitting to their present stature as the trousers or the dresses they wore when they were youngsters.

Childhood dreams are wonderful for children; but when we keep clinging to them in our middle years, they can make failures of us all. This is not because the childhood dreams are wrong — it is rather that we misunderstand their function.

As children, most of us have built a childish fairyland, under the heady illusion that we might grow up and live in it.

Perhaps we have built air castles of success and fame. We may have seen ourselves as renowned artists, writers, actors or musicians; as rich and powerful business executives; as revered professors or honored governors; as inventors or scientists or engineers swathed in acclaim. We built lofty towers in our dreams and flew the pennants of success from dizzy pinnacles.

Such dreams are not without a purpose. It is right for youth to set its sights on the highest spires. For thus youth's energies are released in all their boundlessness. Without such aspirations, youth's energies might lie dormant.

A boy who could not in his childish dreams see himself on a brilliant stage in Carnegie Hall might never give his talent a mighty opportunity at the piano.

A girl who could not see the "great American novel" in the

---
* From Whitman, Howard: *Your Middle Years,* pp. 14-17. Des Moines, Iowa, The Register and Tribune Syndicate, 1961.

fairyland of her future might never sweat out those long, long hours of learning to write.

A youngster who could not see himself as the president of a vast corporation might not go out on the front lawn at the age of 8 to open his first lemonade stand.

These dreams are the power that makes youth go. They are the aspirations that carry youth bravely (sometimes dare-devilishly) into an uncertain future; they are the goads that prod youth over the obstacles of failure and bring out of youth the best it has to offer.

Does it matter if the goals of childhood are not attained? The poet Robert Browning wrote:

> "Ah, but a man's reach should exceed his grasp,
> Or what's a heaven for?"

By bringing out the best that is in an individual, the dream has served its purpose.

But then it is weaning time. Somewhere in the middle years we must let go of the dream. We must, in our maturity, recognize the dream for what it really is: A childhood spur to get us on our way, a goad.

Now that we have done our best (or at least made a good attempt), more goading is superfluous — it merely causes pain.

But beyond that, it is time that we as middle-aged adults perceive the reality behind the dream. It is time to diagnose the dream.

We know now, from life's experience, that the fame that meant so much is in itself no route to happiness; that the wealth, the acclaim, the celebrity we may have dreamed of so longingly — all these have little to do with the inner peace and depth of satisfaction, the self-realization, which now reveal themselves to us as the truly worth-while goals of life.

We might take a cue from St. Paul, in his First Letter to the Corinthians: "When I was a child, I spoke as a child, I understood as a child, I thought as a child; but when I became a man, I put away childish things."

In middle age, we may say in our inner thoughts, "The dream

was fine. It was suitable to childhood. It gave me the zest and courage, it spurred me to put forth the effort to accomplish the most I could in life. Now it is time to 'put away childish things' and take advantage of the vast opportunities opening up to me for the achievement of even greater goals in life.

"Rich and famous I may never be, powerful never, a celebrity never — but I have a good chance to become wise, to develop myself to the fullest into a warm and loving human being, to find within me an attunement to my world and my fellow man and God; to savor life and to enjoy life in its deepest essence as I never have and never could before."

Anne Morrow Lindbergh has written, "Perhaps one can at last in middle age be completely oneself. And what a liberation that would be!"

Liberation, indeed. But many middle-aged men and women are not ready to be liberated. They don't really like themselves enough to be themselves. They are caught up in the losing game of trying to be 10 or 15 years younger — failing to recognize that in falling for this fetish of youth worship, they are not only rejecting themselves but writing off their future.

Men are ridiculous enough when they attempt at 50 to dress and act as though they were 25. But with women the fallacy is even more pitiable, often more ludicrous, and sometimes physically and mentally devastating.

Dr. Marion Hilliard of Women's College Hospital in Toronto declares, "Women whose sole sustaining asset has been their appearance are the most pathetic of all . . . We all know wretched old women with orange hair, round spots of rouge and a determinedly girlish cackle. They are the saddest spectacles of the human race. I know them as a doctor because they are ravaged inside with the symptoms of fear — tremors, bowel and bladder irregularity, dyspepsia, and insomnia."

What do we accomplish by our idolatry of youth except to condemn ourselves to inevitable decline once youth has passed? Instead of finding new glories and new satisfaction in each succeeding year toward life's fulfillment, we become panicky and attempt pathetically and clownishly to bring back, or at least to simulate, the outward face of youth.

Youth has passed, but we are determined to say it isn't so. And thus we defeat ourselves. For as middle-agers we could hardly pass as anything better than second-class youths. And at the same time, we miss the opportunity to be first-class middle-aged adults.

In middle age we have a greater chance at success than we ever had. For it is a realistic success at living rather than youth's frantic race. Its goals are simple, friendly goals, attainable within. Success in middle age becomes personal rather than competitive.

Dr. A. W. MacLeod, associate director of the Mental Hygiene Institute in Montreal, comments, "Some people are overwhelmed when this idea [of middle age] hits them. But the really mature person looks forward to middle age when he will be fully committed to life.

"Unlike the young, the mature middle-aged person is aware of his own limitations, but this awareness doesn't floor him. Instead, he becomes realistic about his goals — and therefore has a very good chance of achieving them."